1/26/66

D1236223

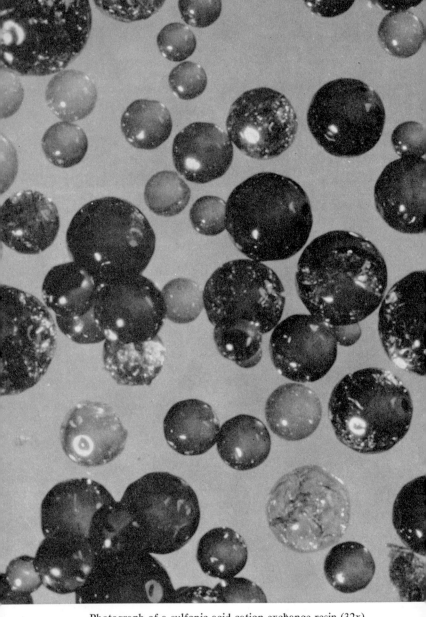

Photograph of a sulfonic acid cation-exchange resin (32x).

Elements of
Ion Exchange

ROBERT KUNIN
Rohm & Haas Company, Philadelphia

REINHOLD PUBLISHING CORPORATION
New York

CHAPMAN & HALL, LTD., *London*

To Edith, Anne, and David

PREFACE

The use of ion exchange has become so widespread in industry and for domestic purposes throughout the world that there is scarcely an industry or an individual that does not employ or that is not affected by this technique. Although many books have been written on the topic of ion exchange, most of these have been written for the expert, the specialist, and the graduate chemist.

The author's experience in the field of ion exchange has indicated that there is a definite need for a book devoted to this topic that is not written for the expert or specialist, but for the uninitiated who have only a slight background of basic chemistry. For example, many mechanical, civil, and sanitary engineers are involved in ion-exchange technology through their activities in water and sewage treatment and power generation. In addition, many non-chemists are employed in the operation of domestic ion-exchange water-softening services and industrial ion-exchange equipment. As a result of many discussions with these people, the author has found a keen desire on their part to achieve a better understanding of ion-exchange technology. All too often, many of them are blindly following operating instructions with, however, a genuine thirst for some understanding of the principles involved in their operations and of the other aspects of ion-exchange technology.

The author has had the opportunity over the past decade to lecture on the topic of ion exchange before those people enumerated above and before high school science teachers, physicians, and various non-science groups. As a result of this activity, it has become quite apparent that an introductory book on the subject of ion exchange would serve a most useful purpose. The material contained in this book has been arranged and digested in a manner that the author has found from his experience will fit the need of those for whom the book is designed.

The author wishes to express his deep appreciation to the Rohm & Haas Company for the encouragement given him during the writing of this book. The author also is deeply indebted to Drs. G. Bodamer, S. Fisher, N. Frisch, A. Preuss, Mr. McGarvey and Mr. C. Dickert for their invaluable assistance in the writing of several chapters.

ROBERT KUNIN

Philadelphia, Pa.
January, 1960

CONTENTS

1. HISTORICAL REVIEW

Many substances when dissolved in water permit the resulting solution to conduct a current of electricity and thereby are termed "electrolytes." The ability of these solutions to conduct a current is due to the formation of small positively and negatively charged particles called "ions." The positively charged ions are called "cations" and the negatively charged ions are called "anions." When an electrolyte such as common table salt, sodium chloride (NaCl), is dissolved in water, an equal number of both anions (chloride ions, Cl^-) and cations (sodium ions, Na^+) are present in solution in order to satisfy the Law of Electroneutrality which in essence states that there can be no excess of one type of electrical charge over the other present in a solution of an electrolyte.

Most natural substances in contact with water dissolve to some extent and thereby give rise to a solution containing such charged particles. Although the presence of ions is essential to all living processes in the animal and plant kingdoms, they pose problems on many occasions. The inability to obtain suds when washing with soap in many areas is due to the presence of calcium and magnesium cations. The staining of the porcelain fixtures and clothes in domestic washing operations is due to minute traces of copper and iron in the water supply. The inability to utilize brackish and sea water for agricultural and drinking purposes is a result of the high concentration of the sodium and chloride ions present in such waters.

Water containing dissolved electrolytes may undergo certain changes when in contact with various solids. In certain instances, some of the ions present in the water will exchange for other ions that are present on the surface of or even in the interior of the solid. When this exchange occurs, the total number of charges leaving the solution must equal the total number entering in order that the Law of Electroneutrality be obeyed. This process, in essence, is the phenomenon of ion exchange. In other words, the term "ion exchange" merely denotes the exchange of ions that occurs across the boundary between a solid particle and a liquid. No specific mechanism need be implied.

Ion-exchange phenomena have been occurring on earth ever since water as a liquid existed and its use by man is almost as ancient as civilization itself. Since water has been one of the major factors that have influenced the various civilizations throughout history, methods for treating it were devised and successfully employed during the early periods of history. These methods included treatments with clays, sands, and chars—substances that owe some of their purifying powers to their ion-exchange properties.

Ion exchange was first recognized in 1845 as a physical-chemical phenomenon by Thompson and Way in England during their investigation of the fate of ammonia in soils. These men noted that when manure was applied to soils, the ammonia was adsorbed by the soil in exchange for the potassium and calcium already present on the soil particles. Their explanation was challenged by the eminent German chemist, Baron von Liebig, and proved to be one of three scientific discoveries questioned by this famous chemist.*

Ion-exchange reactions are most important to the farmer since they prevent the loss of such fertilizer nutrients as potash, nitrogen, and phosphates from the soil during the

---

* The others involved his controversies with Pasteur on fermentation and Lawes and Gilbert on the acidulation of bone.

(Courtesy of The Royal Agricultural Society of England)

Figure 1.1. Sir Harry Meysey Thompson, co-discoverer (with Way) of phenomenon of ion exchange—1849.

percolation of rain water. By means of ion-exchange reactions, these nutrients are adsorbed by the soil as ions in exchange for other ions, primarily hydrogen and hydroxyl ions, which are the products of the electrolytic dissociation of water, and are picked up by the root hairs of plants.

Although the phenomenon was considered of utmost importance to the farmer, soil scientist, and the geochemist, its use commercially was not considered for many years. The utilization of ion-exchange phenomena on a commercial scale started at the turn of the twentieth century and stemmed from the work of Gans, a German chemist, who found that both natural and synthetic aluminum silicates could soften water and remove the scale-forming calcium ions from sugar sirups.

The use of the natural and the synthetic aluminum silicates for softening water is still practiced throughout the world both in industry and in the home. One of the natural aluminum silicates employed for water softening is "greensand marl" mined from sedimentary deposits. The material is in essence the fossilized remains of microscopic animal organisms of marine origin. The synthetic material is a dried gel product formed by reacting solutions of alum and sodium silicate.

These materials are employed generally in upright tanks through which the water is passed for treatment. When the material is exhausted, i.e., can no longer adsorb the hardness determining ions (calcium and magnesium), a strong solution of brine is passed through for regeneration purposes. The sodium ions from the brine (sodium chloride, NaCl) displace the hardness ions from the exhausted exchanger. After a rinse with water, the exchanger is ready to soften water again. Because of the limited capacity and stability of the siliceous exchangers, commercial development of ion exchange was limited not only to water softening but also to specific waters.

The first commercial organic ion-exchange materials were developed in the early nineteen thirties and were prepared by the sulfonation of coal. They are still being manufactured and used for water softening and hydrogen cycle operation. Even these new materials failed to increase the industrial utilization of ion exchange. The true industrial era of ion exchange began in 1935 with the synthesis of phenolformaldehyde-based cation and anion exchange resins by Adams and Holmes in England at the Central Research Laboratory of the Dept. of Scientific and Industrial Research (DSIR). Although the industrial significance of this discovery was

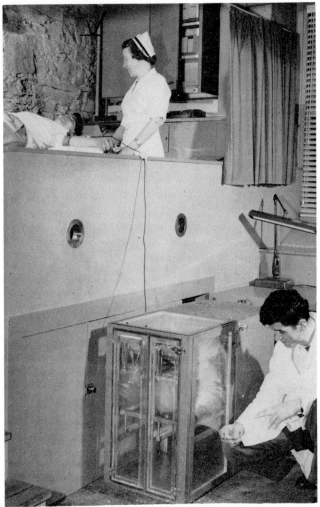

(Courtesy Harvard University News Office)

Figure 1.2. Ion-exchange decalcification of blood.

not too apparent to the English, American interests became quite intrigued with the discovery and in 1940 obtained the rights to the patents. In 1939, research on the synthesis and applications of ion-exchange resins was initiated in the United States and this led to the introduction of the first commercial ion-exchange resins. Success along these lines commercially was followed by a series of new synthetic organic advances including new anion and cation exchange resins in various physical forms designed for a multitude of applications.

Today, the utility of ion exchange phenomena is not restricted to any one field. In the home, one may either use a home water softener or use water treated by a municipal ion-exchange softening plant. The housewife prepares deionized water for her steam iron with a small, self-indicating deionization unit. The sugar sirup she uses in cooking may have been treated by ion exchange. The medicine prescribed by the physician and dispensed by the pharmacist may have been prepared with the aid of an ion-exchange operation, or may consist of an ion-exchange resin itself.

The electric power upon which industry depends and the process water that is also vital may depend directly or indirectly upon ion exchange. Many industrial recovery and waste disposal problems are now nearing solution through an ion-exchange approach.

From the point of view of national defense and public welfare we now find ion exchange to be of vital importance to the collection of blood, isolation and purification of gamma globulin, and to the problem of radioactive waste disposal.

The widespread interest in ion exchange and its general utility during the past decade are direct results of the development and commercial availability of stable and high capacity ion-exchange resins.

From a chronological and historical point of view, the following developments and dates are of considerable interest:

1850-54	Discovery of ion exchange by Thompson and Way in England.
1905	Commercial use of ion exchange developed by Gans in Germany.
1935	Synthetic ion-exchange resins discovered by Adams and Holmes.
1939	Adams and Holmes patents licensed to U. S. industry.
1940	Development of first commercial phenolformaldehyde-based cation and anion exchange resins.
1946	Development of anion exchange resins for ulcer therapy.
1948	Development of styrene-based ion-exchange resins. Development of first unifunctional carboxylic cation exchange resin, an acrylic material. Development of first strong base anion exchange resin.
1950	Development of resins for sodium reduction therapy.
1952	First commercial ion-exchange uranium recovery plant goes on stream.
1955	First commercial uranium resin-in-pulp plant goes on stream. First atomic-powered submarine is launched with an ion exchange deionizing Monobed.
1956	First large-scale commercial ion exchange rare earth separations plant goes on stream.
1957	First commercial liquid ion-exchange operation.

2. THE NATURE OF ION-EXCHANGE MATERIALS

There are many solids, both natural and synthetic, that exhibit the phenomenon described as ion exchange in the last chapter. Soil, humus, wool, cotton, bacterial cells, etc., not generally regarded as ion-exchange materials, are but a few of the naturally occurring substances that are capable of exchanging ions when in contact with a solution containing an electrolyte. Because of the limitations of these materials for specific commercial and research purposes, inorganic and organic ion exchangers have been synthesized.

Regardless of the chemical and physical compositions of the materials exhibiting the phenomenon of ion exchange, they all have one property in common: they are essentially insoluble solid or semisolid electrolytes. Because of this characteristic, particles of these substances will hydrate to some degree when placed in water. If we could examine the hydrated state of these solids, we would find a situation very similar to a solution of an electrolyte, i.e., positive (cations) and negative (anions) some of which are in constant motion and probably in a state of oscillation between ions of the opposite charge. In some of the solids, both of the ionic species are small, simple ions. An insoluble precipitate of silver iodide is an example of this. However, some of these materials are much more complicated and at least one of the ionic species is a part of a huge network of atoms of repeating units called polymer chains. The clay minerals and proteins are naturally occurring examples of such ion-exchange substances. In such cases, only the small ionic species is in a mobile state and the other species is essentially immobile or "fixed," since it is part of the large repeating unit or polymeric chain. These structures may be rigid and orderly, as exemplified by the crystalline zeolite mineral, chabazite. They also may be highly swelling, unoriented structures such as the ion-exchange resins or the amorphous humus contained in peat (Figure 2.1).

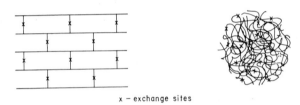

x – exchange sites

Oriented   Unoriented

Figure 2.1. Comparison of hypothetical oriented and unoriented cross-linked ion-exchange structures.

If we put some of this solid into pure water, the material will hydrate and the exchangeable ions will dissociate to some degree and oscillate within a volume dictated by the charge on the ion, the hydration of the ion (most ions associate with the water molecules), and the force of attraction between the exchangeable ion and the fixed ionic charge on the polymeric chain. If some electrolyte is then added to the system, some of these ions will penetrate the oscillation volume and thereby result in an exchange of ions. If the exchanger is now separated from the solution, rinsed, and the resin and solution analyzed, some of the original exchangeable ions in the solid and some of the added electrolyte will be found in both phases. The total number of ionic charges removed from the resin will be equal to that entering the resin. In other words, an equivalency of exchange must be established at all times during the exchange process.

The degree or extent of exchange that occurs during the above process depends upon several factors: (1) the size and valence (charge) of the ions entering into the exchange, (2) the concentration of ions in the water or solution, (3) the nature (both physical and chemical) of the ion-exchange substance, and (4) temperature.

ION-EXCHANGE EQUILIBRIUM

Practically all ion-exchange reactions involving the contacting of a single ion-exchange substance and an electrolyte are reversible; they are true equilibrium reactions and may be represented as follows:

(a) $RA + B^- \rightleftharpoons RB + A^-$
     (R represents anion exchanger, A^- and B^- are anions)

(b) $CR + D^+ \rightleftharpoons DR + C^+$
     (R represents cation exchanger, C^+ and D^+ are cations)

In case (a), the exchange sites of the anion-exchange material are saturated with anions A^- and are contacted with an electrolyte solution containing B^- anions, resulting in an exchange of A^- for B^- anions. The expression also indicates that the reverse may also be accomplished, i.e., an exchanger saturated with B^- anions will, when contacted with an electrolyte solution containing A^- anions, result in an exchange of B^- for A^- anions. Case (b) may be similarly represented. The favored direction of these equilibrium ion-exchange reactions is determined by the relative affinity of the ion exchanger for the ions entering into the exchange reaction. The various ion-exchange equilibria may be expressed in terms of ion selectivity coefficients which are calculated for the equilibrium reaction, a, from the following expression,

$$K_D^* = \left(\frac{A}{B}\right)_o \left(\frac{B}{A}\right)_i ,$$

where K_D is the selectivity coefficient and $\left(\frac{A}{B}\right)_o$ and $\left(\frac{B}{A}\right)_i$ refer to the ratio of the concentrations of ions A and B in the solution phase (o) and resin phase (i), respectively.

The selectivity coefficient depends upon the nature of the ion, the nature of the exchanger, external factors such as temperature, and the degree of saturation of the ion exchange complex. The data contained in Table 2.1 summarize the selectivity coefficients for several ion exchangers and the various anions and cations commonly encountered.

The term selectivity, which is frequently used, is at times somewhat misleading since it is rather meaningless in many instances unless the conditions are defined. Table 2.1 contains data describing the selectivity of various cation and anion exchangers under conditions where the exchange complex contains equal amounts of the two ions entering into the exchange reaction.

Many attempts have been made to establish quantitative expressions that rigorously define and predict the selectivity of ion-exchange materials for the various ions under a wide range of conditions. Although progress has been made, our knowledge to date of such complicated systems is not sufficient to derive expressions that can be employed in a practical manner. In view of this situation, we must fall back

---

* This expression is a Mass Action type of expression for univalent ions. Reader should refer to the references in Appendix 3.

TABLE 2.1. APPROXIMATE ION-EXCHANGE SELECTIVITY COEFFICIENTS

Ion Exchange Material	Ion A	Ion B	Select. Coef. K_A^B (50% sat'd.)*
Cation Exchangers			
Sulfonated styrene-			
divinylbenzene (8%)	H	Li	0.8
	H	Na	2.0
	H	K	3
	H	NH_4	3
	H	Ag	18
	H	Tl	24
	Na	K	1.8
	H	Ca	42
	Ni	Ca	2.5
Sulf-styrene-DVB (5%)	H	Na	1.4
Sulf-styrene-DVB (25%)	H	Na	2.5
Chabazite			
(natural zeolite)	Na	K	14.4
Sodalite			
(natural zeolite)	Na	K	0.06
Anion Exchangers			
Quaternary ammonium			
(strongly basic,			
styrene-DVB)	Cl	F	0.1
	Cl	Br	2.5
	Cl	I	18
	Cl	NO_3	3
	Cl	OH	0.5
	ClO_4	SCN	0.6

* Selectivity coefficient when resin contains equivalent quantities of ions A and B.

upon the following empirical "rules of thumb" as a guide in predicting and planning ion-exchange systems:

(1) At low concentrations (aqueous) and ordinary temperatures, the extent of exchange increases with increasing valency of the exchanging ion: ($Na^+ < Ca^{+2} < Al^{+3} < Th^{+4}$).

(2) At low concentrations (aqueous) ordinary temperatures, and constant valence, the extent of exchange

increases with increasing atomic number of the exchanging ion (Li $<$Na $<$K $<$Rb $<$Cs; Mg $<$Ca $<$Sr $<$Ba).

(3) At high concentrations, the differences in the exchange "potentials" of ions of different valence (Na^+ versus Ca^{+2}) diminish and, in some cases, the ion of lower valence has the higher exchange "potential."

(4) At high temperatures, in non-aqueous media, or at high concentrations, the exchange "potentials" of the ions of similar valence do not increase with increasing atomic number but are very similar, or even decrease.

(5) The relative exchange "potentials" of various ions may be approximated from their activity coefficients —the higher the activity coefficient, the greater the exchange "potential."

(6) The exchange "potential" of the hydrogen (hydronium, H_3O^+, ion) and hydroxyl ions varies considerably with the nature of the functional group and depends on the strength of the acid or base formed between the functional group and either the hydroxyl or hydrogen ion. The stronger the acid or base, the lower the exchange potential.

(7) Organic ions of high molecular weight and complex metallic anionic complexes exhibit unusually high exchange potentials.

(8) As the degree of cross-linking or the fixed ion concentration of an ion-exchange material is lowered, the exchange equilibrium constant approaches unity.

If one examines all the properties of the various inorganic and organic ion exchangers, both synthetic and natural, one finds that these materials constitute a class of electrolytes having many properties quite similar to true solutions, the major difference being that the ion-exchange electrolytes are unable to go into true solution because one of the ionic species is too large. Instead of going into true solution, the exchangers imbibe water and swell, forming a gel-like structure representing a concentrated solution of electrolyte within the structure itself. Depending upon the nature of the exchangeable ions, the cation exchanger may represent either an acid or a salt and the anion exchanger a base or a salt. When the cation exchanger is in the hydrogen form, it behaves as an acid whose strength is determined by the binding energy between the exchangeable hydrogen and the anion structure of the exchanger. When anion exchangers are in hydroxyl form, the anion exchange substances form a series of bases of varying strength. The acid and basic strength of some exchangers are equal to that of sulfuric acid and sodium hydroxide. For example, the acid form of a sulfonic acid cation exchange resin is a strong acid and will react with even solid calcium carbonate and copper metal. The basic or hydroxide forms of some quaternary ammonium anion exchange resins are as strong or even stronger bases than sodium hydroxide.

These acidic and basic structures may be characterized by means of their titration curves. These curves are obtained by measuring the pH (a measure of solution acidity or

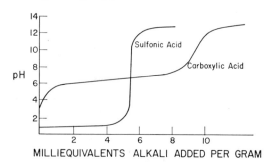

Figure 2.2. Titration curves of cation-exchange resins.

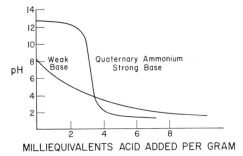

Figure 2.3. Titration curves of anion-exchange resins.

basicity, i.e., the negative logarithm of the hydrogen ion activity) of a suspension of the acid form of a cation exchanger (or the base form of an anion exchanger) as it is progressively neutralized with alkali (or acid in the case of an anion exchanger). Typical curves are shown in Figures 2.2 and 2.3. These curves describe the acidity and basicity of ion exchangers, and also denote their ability to exchange ions at various degrees of solution acidity or basicity (pH).

ION-EXCHANGE KINETICS

Since the speed at which an ion-exchange reaction will take place is of considerable practical as well as theoretical importance, it is well to examine the factors that influence the kinetics of ion exchange. For an exchange of ions involving a porous solid and a solution of an electrolyte the following must occur: (1) the ions in the solution must diffuse to the surface of the solid; (2) they next must diffuse into the structure across a depleted film around the particle; (3) they then undergo exchange; (4) the exchanged ions must then diffuse toward the surface; and (5) finally they must diffuse into the bulk of the solution.

Three diffusional processes may then determine the kinetics of ion exchange. The first, diffusion in the solution phase, does not generally influence the kinetics unless one is dealing with a system involving non-porous solids in a very viscous solution of ionic species of high molecular weight. The second process involves the diffusion across a liquid film about the solid particle. The film is essentially created by the exchange of ions between those present initially at the surface of the particle with those of the solution immediately in contact with the particle. The third involves the diffusion of ions in the solid particle itself.

TABLE 2.2. RELATIVE ION-EXCHANGE RATES

Resin	Time, min. (50% equil. attainment) (hydrogen form of resin)
Sulfonated polystyrene-DVB (8%)	
Na^+	1.5
Ba^{++}	3.0
Al^{+++}	5.5
Th^{++++}	60
organic dyes	days-months
Sulfonated polystyrene-DVB (20%)	
Na	5

Although one might speculate that diffusion through the solid particle would be the controlling rate step, in very dilute solutions the rate of diffusion of electrolyte across the film barrier about the exchanger particle is rate-controlling. As the concentration is increased, the kinetics is determined by both the diffusion across the film and the diffusion in the solid. At still higher concentrations, solid diffusion becomes the sole rate-determining step. Although the concentration ranges noted above will vary with the nature of the exchanger and exchanging ion, film diffusion is usually controlling with concentrations below $0.001N$ (50 ppm as $CaCO_3$) and solid diffusion above $0.3N$ (15,000 ppm). Both processes become controlling in the 0.001 to 0.3N range. An indication of the rates of exchange encountered with ion-exchange systems may be noted in Table 2.2. In addition to the factors of concentration, the nature of the exchanger, and the exchanging ions, such factors as temperature and particle size of the exchanger are also of considerable importance to the kinetics of ion exchange.

PHYSICAL STRUCTURE

The physical structures of ion-exchange substances vary from dense, non-porous materials, in which the exchange of ions is limited to the surface of each particle, to low-density, porous materials in which the exchange of ions may occur throughout the entire particle. The micas are examples of the former and commercial ion-exchange resins and porous zeolitic minerals such as chabazite are examples of the latter.

However, under certain conditions the porous exchangers have exchange properties which indicate that only the surface of the material is available for exchange. This phenomenon is encountered with ions which are so large that their diffusion through the exchanger particle becomes infinitesimally slow or cannot occur at all. The porous type exchangers behave, to some extent, as ionic sieves or screens permitting small ions to diffuse into their structure and excluding the large ones.

Such behavior of the porous exchangers, particularly the ion-exchange resins, is consistent with the model previously described. These materials are essentially high polymer polyelectrolyte structures consisting of chains of atoms tied together by cross-linking chemical structures. The small diffusible and exchangeable ions are only loosely associated with the oppositely charged groups, which are a part of the polymeric chain and are hence non-diffusible. When placed

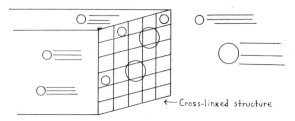

Figure 2.4. Screening of large ions by cross-linked ion-exchange structure (ionic sieve effect).

in water, these materials hydrate and swell until the osmotic forces within the structure balance that of the outside solution. The structure would swell indefinitely and go into solution were it not for the cross-links holding the polymeric polyelectrolyte chains together. The degree of swelling is dependent also upon the nature of the exchangeable ions. One may therefore visualize the structure of these hydrated and swollen exchangers as a three dimensional, open-cellular swollen ball of thread that cannot be unravelled. Although the distances between diffusional barriers of the network are not rigid, they are sufficient to result in the exclusion of large ions (Figure 2.4). The restrictive nature or the porosity of these exchangers may be varied considerably during the synthesis of the ion-exchange resins; that is, one may design exchangers of varying porosity which not only affects its ability to exchange large ions but also alters the kinetics and selectivity of the exchange. This will be discussed in a later chapter.

ION-EXCHANGE CAPACITY

As might be expected, one of the most important properties of an ion-exchange material is its capacity to exchange ions. Although this is rather elementary, it is quite surprising to note the extensive misuse of the term "capacity." The capacity of an ion-exchange material is equal to the number of fixed ionic sites that are capable of entering into an ion-exchange reaction. The ion-exchange capacity of a substance is usually expressed as milliequivalents per gram of substance. In order to distinguish this value from other capacity measurements, the term "total exchange capacity" is sometimes employed; however, the term, "cation exchange capacity" (C.E.C.) is recommended for cation exchange materials and "anion exchange capacity" (A.E.C.) for anion exchange materials.

From a theoretical point of view, it is sometimes of importance to express the capacity of an ion-exchange material in terms of the number of exchangeable ions per unit of water present in the fully hydrated material. This capacity is usually referred to as the "fixed ion concentration."

In any capacity measurements associated with an ion-exchange material, the reference state is quite important, since the weight, volume, or water content of the exchanger will vary with the nature of the ions initially saturating the exchange sites. In view of this, the reference states of the strongly acidic or basic exchangers are usually the sodium and chloride salts, respectively. For the weakly acid and basic exchangers, the standard states are normally the acid and free base forms, respectively. These standard or reference states have been chosen since they represent reproducible and stable drying and weighing forms.

THE DONNAN MEMBRANE EQUILIBRIUM

Ion-exchange materials exhibit an unusual property other than ion exchange when immersed in a solution of an electrolyte. For example, if the sodium form of a strongly acidic cation-exchange material is immersed in a solution of sodium chloride, some sodium chloride will diffuse into the solid; however, at equilibrium the concentration of sodium chloride inside the exchanger, $(NaCl)_i$, will be less than that outside, $(NaCl)_o$. In other words,*

$$[NaCl]_i < [NaCl]_o$$

The unequal distribution of sodium chloride across the exchanger-solution interface may be explained by means of the *Donnan Membrane Theory*. This theory applies to the equilibria across membranes on one side of which is an electrolyte *one* of whose ionic species cannot diffuse across the membrane, and the other side of which is an electrolyte *all* of whose ionic species can diffuse. An ion-exchange system may be considered as a Donnan system, since the exchanger-solution interface serves as a membrane. According to the Donnan Theory, equilibrium is attained when the product of the diffusible ionic concentrations on one side of the membrane is equal to that on the other. Therefore, in the above example, equilibrium will be attained when

$$[Na]_i \times [Cl]_i = [Na]_o \times [Cl]_o.$$

Since there is initially a high $[Na]_i$ within the exchanger by virtue of its exchange capacity, only a small amount of NaCl need diffuse into the exchanger phase to satisfy the above equilibrium requirement. In other words, the exchangeable sodium ions originally present in the exchanger are no different from those in the sodium chloride solution and therefore must be considered in the equilibrium. If we take the case of a strong acid cation-exchange resin having a total capacity of 5 milliequivalents per gram or a fixed ion concentration of $10M$ (10 equivalents per 1000 g water), we will find that only a trace of salt will diffuse into the exchanger phase if the material is immersed in a $0.1N$ salt solution.

---

* The brackets denote concentration.

At equilibrium, the external concentration will be a little less than 0.1 and the internal NaCl concentration will be approximately $0.001N$. In other words, little diffusion of free electrolyte into an ion-exchange material occurs until the concentration of the solution contacting the exchange approaches that of the fixed ion concentration of the exchanger. Exchangers of high capacity have the property of excluding free electrolyte. The significance of this phenomenon will be discussed in a later chapter.

3. THE STRUCTURE AND SYNTHESIS OF ION-EXCHANGE MATERIALS*

For a material to operate in ion-exchange processes it basically must (1) contain functional groups or sites where ions in solution can replace ions attached to the material itself, and (2) be insoluble in water or other solvents in which it is to be employed. In addition to these features there are other properties which the material must have if it is to be truly useful in a commercial application. These are enumerated below:

(1) The functional groups must be present in reasonably large numbers per unit weight or, frequently more important, per unit volume. This property is usually thought of in terms of ion-exchange capacity and expressed as milli-equivalents of exchangeable ion per gram of dry resin or per milliliter of wet resin.

(2) The functional groups must be accessible to ions in solution. Generally, this means that the material must permit solution to penetrate throughout its structure; otherwise ions will be unable to approach the exchange sites even though they may be present. We usually think of this property as the porosity of the structure and express it in terms of the moisture-holding capacity calculated as per cent moisture or per cent solids of the material equilibrated with water. It is also necessary that the material possess pores large enough to admit at least the more common ions such

---

* This chapter was written in cooperation with Dr. George W. Bodamer of the Rohm & Haas Co.

as H^+, Na^+, K^+, Ca^{++}, Mg^{++}, OH^-, Cl^-, NO_3^-, $SO_4^=$, etc., in their hydrated forms.

(3) The functional groups must be ionic or capable of rearrangement to an ionizable structure.

(4) The ion-exchange material must be physically and chemically durable over a wide range of conditions. Ideally, it should not be affected by strong acids, strong bases, concentrated salts, oxidizing or reducing substances, or extremes of temperature. That is to say, the material should not break down physically, decompose chemically, nor swell excessively when exposed to such conditions. Actually no material at present available possesses all these attributes; but many materials do show considerable resistance to most of these potentially deleterious conditions.

(5) The material must be available in useful form. For the conventional column operations, particles in the range of 0.3 to 1.19 mm diameter are most desirable. For certain applications, particularly in the pharmaceutical and chromatographic analytical fields, finer particles, as small as 0.04 mm diameter, are used.

NATURAL ION-EXCHANGE MATERIALS

A tremendous variety of naturally occurring substances, including living animal and plant tissue and the constituents of the soil (minerals and decomposed animal and plant tissue) possess the ability to exchange ions. In fact, this ion-exchange ability is an essential part of the functioning of most of these substances in nature. A partial list of natural substances possessing ion-exchange properties is given on the following page.

Of all these substances, and many more, only the zeolite minerals have a sufficiently satisfactory combination of the above-mentioned characteristics—reasonable concentration of functional groups, accessibility of exchange sites, reasonable durability, and suitable particle size—to permit their

Polysaccharides	Proteins
algic acid	casein
pectin	keratin (wool, horn)
carragheen	collagen, gelatin
potato starch	spongin
corn starch	Humus in soil
flour	
cellulose	
wood	
paper	
straw	

Minerals

Clay minerals	*Zeolite minerals*
vermiculite	chabazite
montmorillonite	heulandite
kaolinite	analcite
attapulgite, etc.	sodalite

use as ion exchangers on a commercial scale. Without going into detail on the crystallographic differences in these minerals, they can be considered to be complex aluminosilicates with more or less Na^+, K^+, Ca^{++}, Mg^{++} and other associated cations. The schematic diagram gives a very rough idea of their structure:

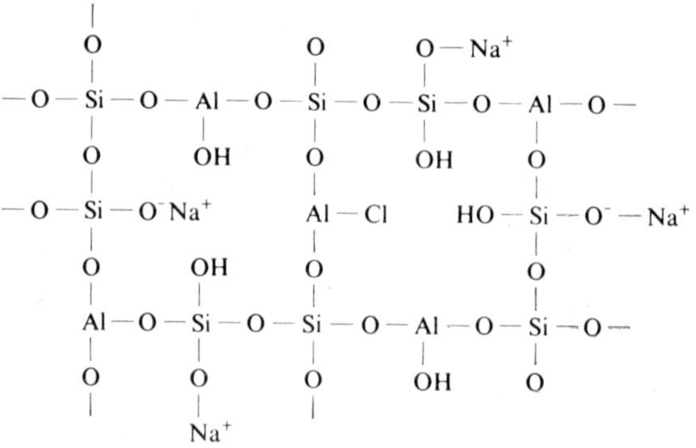

As the diagram indicates, some at least of these minerals are capable of exchanging anions, but by far their greatest field of application is in cation exchange, specifically water softening. Their strongest selling point is their cheapness. They are relatively low in capacity, compared to resinous exchangers, and are deficient in chemical stability, decomposing in waters that are slightly acidic (below pH 6.5) or slightly basic (above pH 8.0) and in low-silica waters. Despite these limitations considerable quantities are in use and are still being sold in this country. Commercial products of this type are referred to as greensands, zeolites, etc.

ION-EXCHANGE MATERIALS DERIVED FROM NATURAL PRODUCTS

Over the years, many enterprising chemists have sought to make use of natural products, because of their inherent ion-exchange properties or simply because they were cheap, as starting materials for improved products—products with higher capacity or greater durability. Even a cursory glance at the literature uncovers such oddities as sulfonated olive pits and aminated cow horns.

All this work yielded only one commercially important product—sulfonated coal. This material, which came into use shortly before the advent of synthetic ion-exchange resins, contained sulfonic acid ($-SO_3H$) as well as carboxylic acid ($-COOH$) groups, the latter being present in the original coal and also arising as a result of oxidation by the concentrated sulfuric acid employed. The strong acid groups permitted operation in the hydrogen cycle for the first time and opened the way for complete deionization of solutions. Sulfonated coal is cheap, has fair capacity, and, because of its relatively greater versatility than the zeolites, is still in fairly wide use.

A product which may be placed in this general category, as being derived from a natural substance, is a reaction product of quebracho tannin (an extract of the bark of a South American tree) with formaldehyde and sodium sulfite. While it functioned satisfactorily in certain waters, continued experience revealed that there were too many slightly alkaline waters which tended to dissolve the product, and it was soon superseded by the truly synthetic resins.

SYNTHETIC ION-EXCHANGE MATERIALS

The so-called synthetic gel zeolites are prepared by mixing solutions of sodium silicate and aluminum sulfate. The gels are dried and washed free of sodium sulfate to give products which are chemically similar to the natural products. The synthetic approach enables one to vary the properties somewhat and provides a source of more uniform material than is available from nature. Considerable quantities of synthetic zeolites are still sold.

Recently there has been some interest in exchangers made by reacting zirconium oxychloride with sodium tungstate or phosphate in slightly acidic solutions. The resulting gel structure is a network of zirconium and tungsten or phosphate atoms linked together with oxygen atoms. The hydrogen ion of the hydroxyl groups attached to the zirconium atoms is replaceable by other cations. This substance has been used to separate alkali metal ions by successive elution with NH_4Cl solutions of increasing concentration.

A very large number of reactions yielding organic resinous materials containing functional groups has been investigated, systematically and otherwise, during the past twenty years.

Resin syntheses in general can be classified as condensation polymerizations and addition polymerizations. A condensation polymerization is one in which molecules of two or more different compounds combine to form a somewhat larger molecule with the elimination of a small, simple molecule such as H_2O, HCl, etc. An example of such a reaction is that between phenol and formaldehyde. The first step may be considered to be the formation of simple compounds of the type shown in the following equation:

Phenol   *formaldehyde*

Actually, except under rigorously controlled conditions, this reaction proceeds much further to give very large molecules or resins.

Such resins are three-dimensional networks which are insoluble and thus provide one of the prime requisites of an ion-exchange resin.

Addition polymerization is one in which two or more molecules of the same compound or similar compounds combine to form a large molecule. No small molecules are eliminated and the final weight of the product is equal to the sum of the weight of all the molecules entering into the polymerization.

Among organic compounds, those which contain double or triple bonds between carbon atoms ($C = C$ and $-C \equiv C-$) (unsaturated compounds) are polymerizable. The $CH_2 = CH-$ group is called the vinyl group, and compounds containing it are the starting materials for some of the most important present-day plastics as well as ion-exchange resins. A typical example of addition polymerization is provided by styrene:

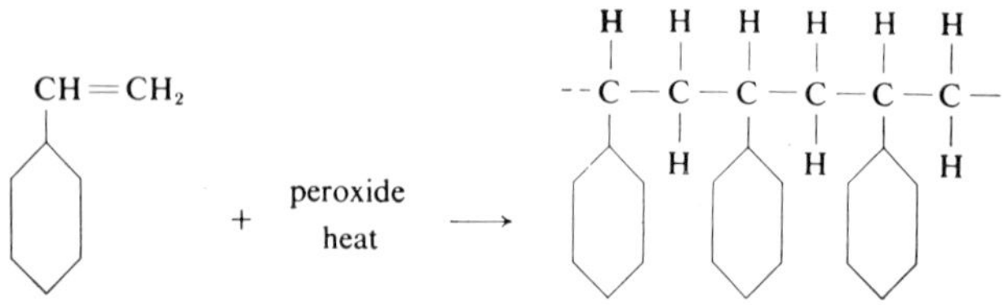

Styrene   **Polystyrene**

If the reactive compound or monomer has only one double bond, only linear polymers result. Linear polymers are soluble in solvents and melt at elevated temperatures. By copolymerizing with a monomer containing two or more double bonds a three-dimensional, insoluble, infusible resin results:

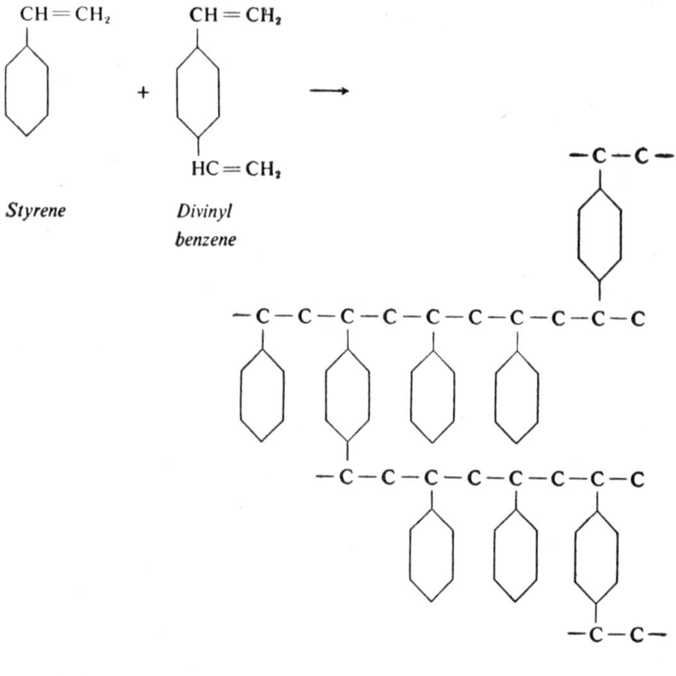

Styrene   **Divinyl benzene**

Here, again, is a backbone on which to construct an ion-exchange resin.

Resins Made by Condensation Reactions

Phenolic resins are historically important, for they were the first synthetic resinous exchangers introduced commercially. While they dominated the field for some ten years, they have now been largely superseded by resins based on styrene and acrylate polymers.

Cation Exchangers. One of the earliest products was a phenolformaldehyde-sodium sulfite condensate. The ingredients were mixed to form a homogeneous solution. After an initial heating period, the reaction became exothermic and was controlled by cooling. As condensation proceeded, the entire, homogeneous solution became increasingly viscous. When it reached a thick, syrupy consistency it was poured into shallow pans, and then heated in ovens until the resin gelled to a hard brittle mass. This was ground and screened to the desired particle size. The resin had the structure:

The functional groups are the —CH_2SO_3Na groups. The phenolic —OH groups are functional as cation-exchange sites only in solutions which are considerably more alkaline than most natural waters.

Resins of this type soon came to be used widely in water softening (Na-Ca cycle) and in two-bed deionization (H cycle). While their capacity was no better than that of the zeolites, they could be employed in the hydrogen cycle and with waters where the latter could not, and in respect to physical properties and durability they were superior to sulfonated coal.

Nuclear sulfonic resin is a name which has been applied to types in which the $-SO_3H$ group is attached directly to the phenol ring. These resins are made by sulfonating phenol with concentrated H_2SO_4, adding formaldehyde, and finishing much as was described above.

Resins of this type were widely used in the past, especially in Europe, but since they suffer from the same limitations as the other phenolic condensates they are disappearing from the scene.

Anion Exchangers. One of the earliest anion-exchange resins was made by condensing a phenol, formaldehyde, and triethylene tetramine (TETA); this product was processed in much the same fashion as the phenol sulfonic acid resins:

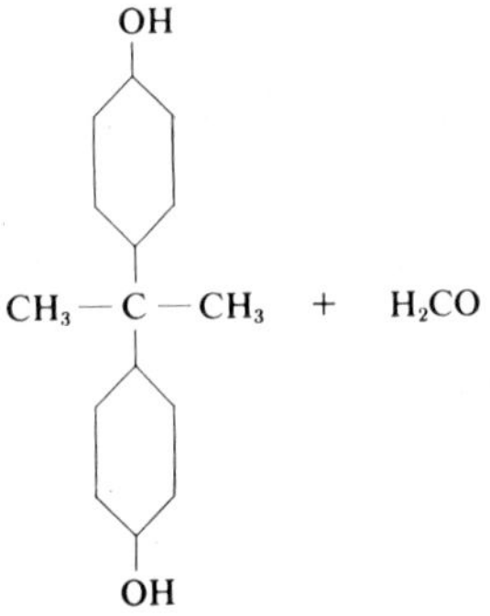

Diphenol

$$+ \quad NH_2-CH_2-CH_2-NH-CH_2-CH_2-NH-CH_2-CH_2NH_2 \quad \longrightarrow$$

TETA

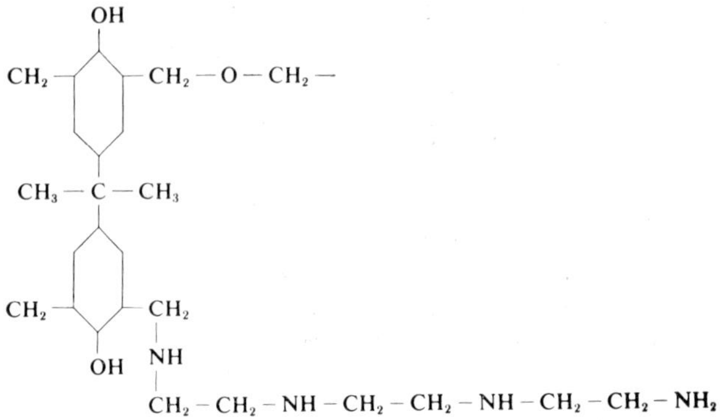

$$CH_2-CH_2-NH-CH_2-CH_2-NH-CH_2-CH_2-NH_2$$

These resins are low-cost, high-capacity, weak-base resins whose functional groups are secondary ($-NH-$) and primary ($-NH_2$) amine groups. They have been widely used in two-bed deionization systems. However, the newer styrene-based anion exchangers are superior in stability. These resins are still used in specialties, particularly in the pharmaceutical industry.

Resins Made by Vinyl Polymerization

Cation Exchangers. The more important cation-exchange resins are made by the sulfonation of a styrene-divinyl benzene copolymer. Styrene and divinyl benzene (DVB) are thoroughly mixed, and an organic peroxide is dissolved in the mixture. This solution is poured into an equal or larger quantity of water and dispersed into droplets throughout the aqueous phase by agitation. To the water there have previously been added small amounts of water-soluble compounds which have the ability to stabilize the suspension, that is, prevent the droplets of organic liquid from coalescing into larger masses. The average size of the droplets may be made larger or smaller by regulating the speed of stirring and the amount of stabilizing agent.

The suspension is then heated until polymerization (an exothermic reaction) begins, after which the temperature is controlled by cooling. The droplets increase in viscosity, pass through sticky, then rubbery stages and, finally, become hard spheres as the polymer grows. The polymerization is completed by continued heating in the reaction vessel or (after filtering the beads out of the water) in ovens.

The styrene-DVB beads are now transferred to another vessel where they are heated with concentrated sulfuric acid or other sulfonating agents such as chlorosulfonic acid.

$$-CH-CH_2-CH-CH_2-$$

$$+ \quad H_2SO_4 \quad \longrightarrow$$

large excess

$$+ \quad H_2O$$

$$SO_3H \qquad -CH-CH_2-$$

Between 8 and 10 $-SO_3H$ groups are introduced for every 10 benzene rings.

The residual sulfuric acid is diluted by the slow addition of water (to avoid too rapid swelling of the resin which may cause shattering); the diluted acid is filtered off, the beads are washed with water and finally neutralized with NaOH or Na_2CO_3.

$$-CH-CH_2 \qquad + \quad NaOH \quad \longrightarrow \qquad -CH-CH_2- \qquad + \quad H_2O$$

$$SO_3H \qquad \qquad SO_3Na$$

The neutralized product is backwashed to remove fines.

In addition to providing a product of superior ion exchange capacity, the above process is faster, simpler to operate, and gives higher yields in the desired particle range than the phenolic condensation reactions. Furthermore, it is a simple matter to vary the porosity of the final product by regulating the ratio of DVB to styrene.

This type of resin has much to recommend it. It has high

capacity. Its strongly ionized sulfonate group enables it to "split neutral salts" when operating in the hydrogen cycle,

$$RSO_3^- \; H^+ + Na^+ + Cl^- \rightleftharpoons RSO_3^- \; Na^+ + H^+ + Cl^-$$

and gives it a rapid rate of exchange. It is very durable in solutions of all degrees of concentration and of acidity or alkalinity. It does not have highly specific affinities for different ions (which may or may not be an advantage, depending on the application), but its highly dissociated nature requires considerably more than equivalent amounts of acid for complete regeneration in the hydrogen cycle (the reverse of the above equation).

By varying the degree of cross-linking in these sulfonated copolymers of styrene and divinylbenzene, a series of resins of varying swelling ratios or porosity may be obtained. A typical series is represented in the following table. As the amount of cross-linking agent (DVB) is decreased, the swelling ratio and moisture-holding capacity increase.

TABLE 3.1. PROPERTIES OF AN ION EXCHANGE SYSTEM AT
VARIOUS DEGREES OF CROSS-LINKING

Resin	% DVB	% Moisture	CAPACITY meq./g	meq./ml
A	4.0	62.6	4.81	1.27
B	8.5	48.6	4.79	1.87
C	10.0	43.1	5.07	2.30
D	12.5	40.8	5.12	2.47
E	15.0	35.4	4.81	2.65

An altogether different type of cation-exchange resin, depending for its functionality on the presence of weakly ionized carboxylic acid groups, may be prepared by suspension copolymerization of methacrylic acid and divinylbenzene (DVB).

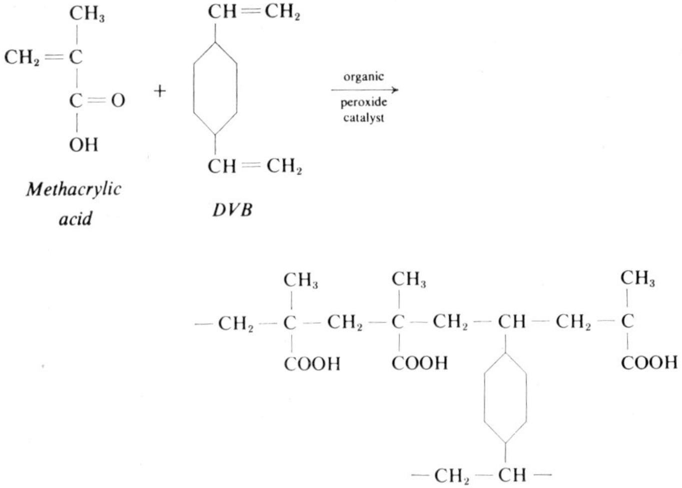

$$CH_2 = C \begin{matrix} CH_3 \\ | \\ | \\ C=O \\ | \\ OH \end{matrix}$$

Methacrylic acid

DVB

organic peroxide catalyst

$$-CH_2-\underset{\underset{COOH}{|}}{\overset{\overset{CH_3}{|}}{C}}-CH_2-\underset{\underset{COOH}{|}}{\overset{\overset{CH_3}{|}}{C}}-CH_2-CH-CH_2-\underset{\underset{COOH}{|}}{\overset{\overset{CH_3}{|}}{C}}$$

$$-CH_2-CH-$$

The weakly acidic —COOH groups have little or no salt-splitting capacity; that is to say, the hydrogen form of the resin will remove few or no cations from neutral salt solutions. However, in alkaline waters these resins will remove cations equivalent to the alkalinity present and can then be regenerated with acid very efficiently because of the weak acidity:

$$2RCOONa + H_2SO_4 \rightarrow 2RCOOH + 2Na^+ + SO_4^=$$

In the form of the sodium salt, the carboxylic resin can be employed for softening, but because of a powerful affinity for Ca^{++} regeneration with Na^+ directly is most difficult:

$$2RCOONa + Ca^{++} + 2Cl^- \leftrightarrows (RCOO)_2 Ca + 2Na^+ + 2Cl^-$$

Thus the water-conditioning applications for this type of resin are somewhat limited; instead, they have been more widely employed in other fields such as the recovery and purification of antibiotics, the deionization of sugar solution, the removal of sodium from persons suffering from faulty elimination of sodium through the kidneys, etc.

Anion Exchangers. The first truly strong base ion-exchange material to be developed was prepared by the suspension copolymerization of styrene and DVB, much as in the first step of the styrene-based cation-exchange resins. The polymer beads are treated with chloromethyl ether, using a catalyst such as aluminum chloride or zinc chloride, which introduces $-CH_2Cl$ groups on the benzene rings. The product is then aminated with trimethylamine (TMA):

$$-CH-CH_2 \quad + \quad CH_3OCH_2Cl \quad \xrightarrow{\text{AlCl}_3} \quad -CH-CH_2 \quad + \quad CH_3OH$$

(*cross-linked*) *Chloromethyl* CH_2Cl
  polymer   *ether*

$$-CH-CH_2 \quad + \quad CH_3-\underset{\underset{CH_3}{|}}{N}-CH_3 \quad \longrightarrow \quad -CH-CH_2$$

  CH_2Cl *TMA* CH_2

$$CH_3-\overset{+}{\underset{\underset{CH_3}{|}}{N}}-CH_3Cl^-$$

The highly ionized quaternary ammonium group,

$-CH_2-\overset{\overset{CH_3}{|}}{\underset{\underset{CH_3}{|}}{N^+}}-CH_3$, is its functional group. In the hydroxide

form this resin has the basicity of NaOH.

The outstanding features of these strong base resins are rapid rate of exchange and high basicity. They are capable of removing, from solution, the most weakly acidic substances, in particular silica, $SiO_2 \cdot H_2O$ or H_2SiO_3. Because of their salt-splitting capacity they can be used in reverse deionization (anion exchanger in OH^- form before cation exchanger in H^+ form) and in Monobeds with carboxylic cation exchangers.

The weaknesses of strong base resins are (1) an inescapable instability of quaternary ammonium groups which causes them to revert to tertiary or other weak amine structures, especially at elevated temperatures and when in the OH^- form; and (2) fouling with organic matter in natural waters. In this latter process, high molecular weight materials, such as the so-called humic acids, which are vegetable decomposition products, are so firmly adsorbed on the surface that the exchange sites within the bead are screened off from the ions in solution, making it impossible to utilize the exchange capacity efficiently.

The porosity of these anion-exchange resins may be controlled, as in the case of the cation-exchange resins, by adjusting the amount of cross-linking agent (DVB). The resulting resin contains pores large enough to permit penetration of the organic matter into the resin particle. Thus the internal exchange centers are not blocked off by the adsorption of a relatively small amount of organic matter on the surface. Because of the higher porosity, the more porous resins find use in the removal of organic matter from natural waters for the preparation of the highest quality deionized water and in the decolorization of sugar solutions.

Weak Base Anion Exchangers. Production of these resins starts with the copolymerization of styrene and DVB, continues with chloromethylation, and is completed by amination with an amine such as diethylene triamine, DETA.

$$-CH-CH_2$$

$$CH_2Cl$$

$$+ \quad NH_2-CH_2-CH_2-NH-CH_2-CH_2-NH_2$$

DETA

$$\longrightarrow$$

$$-CH-CH_2-$$

$$CH_2-NH-CH_2-CH_2-NH-CH_2-NH_2-HCl$$

After washing with water, the resin is neutralized to the free base form in which it is sold. The functional groups are primary and secondary amino groups.

Theoretical Maximum Capacity

For some time it appeared that, with the existing standard types of exchangers, the upper limit of volume capacity had been reached for all practical purposes. Repeated attempts to squeeze in more functional groups had revealed that, at best, only relatively few more could be introduced and then only at the expense of greatly prolonged reaction times or other extreme conditions. From the applications standpoint, also, it was apparent that increased total capacity gave only diminishing returns in improved operating capacity at any economical regeneration level.

However, it has been shown that even from a theoretical standpoint the existing products had indeed approached very close to the limit. These studies were based on measurements of exchange capacity, moisture content, the true density of the ion-exchange particle, and the number of molecules of water associated with the exchangeable ions. The latter values were obtained from measurements of the amount of water transported through "permselective" membranes during electrolysis. In essence, this work shows that the functional groups and the more important exchangeable ions, when both are hydrated, make up the major part of the volume of a resin particle. The remaining part of the resin, the skeleton to which the functional groups are attached, does not occupy a great deal of volume in the current standard products. Even if some new type of skeleton is found which is still less bulky, one cannot expect a great increase in volume capacity.

The foregoing comments are not to be construed as indicating that there are no new worlds to conquer in the synthesis of ion-exchange resins. They only say that attempts to obtain much higher volume capacities are not likely to be very fruitful. There is still much to be done by way of increasing the physical and chemical stability of granular resins, introducing new and different functional groups which may have special affinities for certain ions, altering certain properties for particular applications, and so on, not to mention the preparation of resins in special forms such as membranes and fibers when and if applications for such materials appear.

ION-EXCHANGE MEMBRANES

Late in the nineteenth century biochemists became aware that the only explanation for many biological phenomena was the existence of natural membranes around cells which permitted the passage through them of cations but not anions, or vice versa. In order to investigate these phenomena further, many of the workers utilized actual membranes from cells, such as the giant axon (portion of a nerve cell) of the squid, or other natural membranous structures such as fruit skins. As these materials were seldom readily obtainable and not very easy to work with, some biochemists began making "models" of such substances by introducing ion-exchange groups into cellulose films, for example. These films had the same "permselective" properties (permitting passage of one species of ion while excluding the other) as exhibited by natural membranes.

Much later it became apparent that such membranes could have more than academic utility provided they were sufficiently strong and durable and contained a high concentration of functional groups. Two important types have been developed. One type (heterogeneous) is made by intimately dispersing finely ground ion-exchange resins throughout a thermoplastic matrix. In the case of a cation-permeable membrane the resin is a sulfonated styrene-DVB type, and in the case of an anion permeable membrane it is of the quaternary type. The matrix may be of polyethylene, polyvinyl chloride, polyvinylidene chloride, natural or synthetic rubbers. The other type (homogeneous) is made by condensation processes using sulfonated phenol and formaldehyde or nitrogen-containing compounds and formaldehyde. The condensates are laid out in thin sheets, with or without supports such as paper or plastic screen, before final gelation to an insoluble form.

Both types of membrane are primarily used in electrochemical processes rather than in conventional ion-exchange applications. They improve the efficiency of electrochemical processes by permitting the ready migration of either cations or anions, but not both, between the electrodes, and by preventing diffusion of the products formed at each electrode toward the other electrode.

ION-EXCHANGE FIBERS

Cellulose fibers have been reacted with a variety of reagents to introduce functional groups which will give cation-exchange or anion-exchange properties. For example, a sulfonic type may be synthesized by the following reactions:

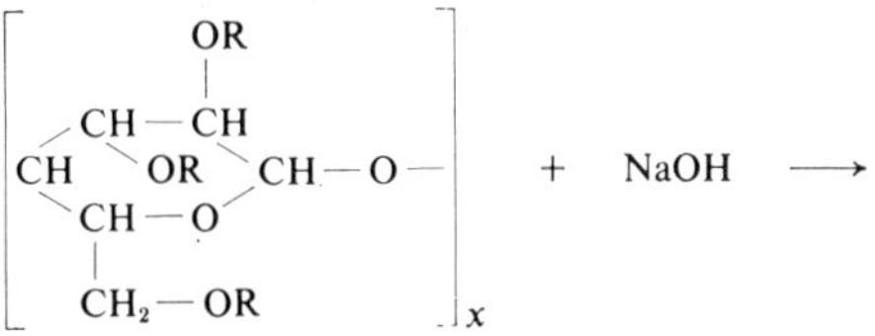

$$\left[\begin{array}{c} OR \\ | \\ CH-CH \\ CH \quad OR \quad CH-O- \\ CH-O \\ | \\ CH_2-OR \end{array}\right]_x \quad + \quad NaOH \longrightarrow$$

modified cellulose
R = Amino-alkyl
    Carboxy alkyl
    Acyl
    Hydrogen

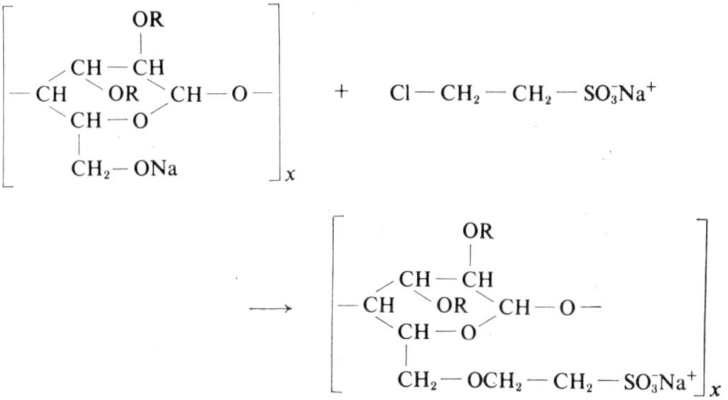

$$\left[\begin{array}{c} OR \\ | \\ CH-CH \\ -CH \quad OR \quad CH-O- \\ CH-O \\ | \\ CH_2-ONa \end{array}\right]_x \quad + \quad Cl-CH_2-CH_2-SO_3^-Na^+$$

$$\longrightarrow \left[\begin{array}{c} OR \\ | \\ CH-CH \\ -CH \quad OR \quad CH-O- \\ CH-O \\ | \\ CH_2-OCH_2-CH_2-SO_3^-Na^+ \end{array}\right]_x$$

It has been suggested that such fibers may be advantageous in specialized applications, for example, when woven into filter clothes, but as yet there have been no large commercial applications.

4. TESTING AND EVALUATION OF ION-EXCHANGE MATERIALS*

GENERAL CONSIDERATIONS

The usefulness of an ion-exchange material is dependent upon both its chemical and its physical properties. Hence, for a complete characterization of an ion exchanger a number of individual tests of specific properties must be made and judgment based on the composite properties. This is particularly important since it is possible for a material to have some very desirable characteristic, such as high weight capacity, and at the same time to be of no practical value because of a too high moisture content or swelling ratio. On the other hand, a material may have excellent physical properties but contain functional groups that are too weakly acidic or basic to be of practical use.

In general, the operating characteristics of an ion-exchange resin are primarily dependent upon:

(1) the structure of the functional group
(2) the number of functional groups per unit weight and volume
(3) the porosity (moisture-holding capacity)
(4) the particle size

Specific uses of the polymer may also make some or all of the following properties important:

---

* This chapter was written in cooperation with Dr. Sallie A. Fisher of the Rohm & Haas Co.

(1) pressure drop
(2) hydraulic expansion
(3) volume change between ionic forms
(4) solubility or content of extractable material
(5) color throw

In addition, specific tests may be devised for a special material in a single application; i.e., the uranium capacity of an anion-exchange resin, the streptomycin capacity of a carboxylic cation-exchange resin, and the acid-removal capacity of a weakly basic anion-exchange resin. Such tests are required where the particular application depends on such a complex interaction of properties that it is difficult to make an accurate prediction of resin utility by standard applications tests.

The choice of evaluation tests to be run depends upon the reason why the material is being tested. In general, an evaluation of an ion exchanger is carried out for one of the following reasons:

(1) routine control of the production of ion-exchange materials
(2) evaluation of standard products that have been used
(3) process development and modification
(4) selection of a product for a new application
(5) development of a new product

The categories, which are listed in roughly increasing order of complexity of the testing programs that accompany them, will be discussed separately.

Routine Control

It is the aim of routine production control to obtain sufficient data to prove that a product is satisfactory to sell with the smallest expenditure of time and effort. Methods used on routine control are frequently developed with the objective of giving rapid and reproducible numbers rather than of producing data of scientific value. These numbers should, if possible, be characteristic of the particular product being evaluated so that the shipment of a wrong or inferior product may be avoided.

The most fundamental determinations performed in routine control are the exchange capacity determinations and the moisture determination. With these it is possible to distinguish between the various types of functional groups (sulfonic, carboxylic, quaternary and weak base), and also, in the case of a given functional group, between the different degrees of cross-linking. It is not possible, using the control procedures alone, to distinguish between different types of carboxylic polymers such as, say, the methacrylic acid types and the acrylic acid types, or different types of quaternary groups such as trimethyl amine and dimethyl ethanolamine types. These more subtle differences require research methods.

Routine control differs from research evaluation not only in its emphasis on speed and simplicity but also in that the analysis is done on an "as is" basis. Since it is desirable that the values obtained reflect the state of the material as shipped to the customer, no pretreatment of the sample is customary before determining the weight or volume used in analysis. Thus, for example, the moisture content may differ from that obtained on pretreated samples, as it reflects the draining technique in the plant operation rather than controlled laboratory technique. Further, the measured capacities are based on whatever ionic form the finished plant product is in. In some cases this may be different from the forms preferred for research evaluation.

In addition to the moisture and capacity determinations, other tests, such as density, wet screening, whole bead content, and pressure drop, are run for control purposes where the nature of the product and its end use warrant. Special tests of a single product for a specific application are run only when the standard tests have not provided sufficiently close control to meet the needs of a large application. They are frequently discontinued when sufficient information has been obtained to permit correlation of, say, capacity, moisture content, and effective size with the desired properties.

Evaluation of Standard Materials That Have Been Used

The tests used in the evaluation of used materials are sometimes identical with those used in routine control and are sometimes adapted from more complicated research techniques. The greatest problem in the evaluation of used material arises from the dependence of the properties of an ion-exchange material on the ionic form, since the form of the used material is usually different from that of the material as shipped. It is essential that samples be uniformly representative of the lots from which they are taken, particularly as regards particle size. Their properties are affected to some extent by the sampling method used. Thus, careful consideration must be given to the problems of sampling and pretreatment of used materials. Unless careful control of these variables is maintained, any extensive comparison between new and used material is dangerous. Really valid comparisons may be made only when a representative sample of the original material that has undergone the same pretreatment is compared with a representative sample of the used material.

Process Development and Modification

The aim of a process development may either be the evolution of the best possible new product or the improvement or simplification of an existing product or process. The tests used in following such changes may be the standard control tests, or they may be special tests devised for a specific problem.

In general, in following such a process, the problem of pretreating the resin to obtain a known functional group is not serious, since all samples will be finished in a standard ionic form. Since the moisture content is frequently used as an indication of changes in polymer porosity in process control, hydration of the sample before determination of the dry weight is critical in this case; all samples should be soaked and drained by the standard procedure prior to analysis. Since such analyses are frequently made on small laboratory batches of resin wherein the entire sample may be used in some phases of analyses, the problem of effective size variations is one that must be taken into consideration in all evaluations. No effective substitute for the use of screened cuts in sensitive comparisons has as yet been devised. Where this is not done and a determination of effective size is not made, some qualitative observation of size as compared with the size of standard process material should be included in the evaluation. This comparison is particularly critical when column evaluations are run.

Although one property of the resin may be paramount in a process development, the nature of ion-exchange polymers is such that improvement in one characteristic is frequently accompanied by a deterioration in another. Therefore, while it is tempting in a process development to limit one's evaluation to only the primary property in which improvement is anticipated, samples that do show such improvement must be given a complete evaluation to determine whether or not the other essential variables have remained unchanged.

Selection of a Product for a New Application

The selection of a product for a new application usually is accomplished in a two-step approach. The first involves screening tests of samples already known to have suitable chemical and physical properties for other applications by the use of a special test devised for the new application. Should such screening programs turn up a promising experimental resin, a second stage involving process development would require not only special applications testing but standard methods as well.

Development of a New Product

When a new structure is synthesized, it must be tested in competition with standard products to determine whether or not it shows any advantage over existing products. As our knowledge of ion exchange increases, and in particular as we become more aware of the required properties for a commercial product, the problems of testing a new structure have become more complex.

In the early development stages of ion exchange, the primary emphasis in new product testing was on the search for materials of higher operating capacities. While this is still of interest in the field, considerations involving physical and chemical stability under a variety of conditions, permeability to large ions, specificity for the ions of economic importance in various metallurgical situations or operability at high flow rates or temperatures outweigh capacity alone as a new product objective.

Thus, where formerly a decision could be made on the basis of a few standard tests, the selection of a new product is now a complex, many-faceted procedure, frequently involving the establishment of new test procedures. No compilation such as this could attempt to cover the needs of a research development program. It is primarily dependent on the necessities of the present situation and the ingenuity of the applications chemist in devising tests to determine whether the materials being studied fill the existing requirements. However, such tests must be subject to all the foregoing precautions as to ionic form, hydration, particle size and form if valid conclusions as to the potential of experimental samples are to be drawn.

Since ion-exchange polymers of practical importance are insoluble, three-dimensional networks with homogeneously appended ionic functional groups, their properties are dependent on the nature of the network, and on the kind and concentration of the ionic groups. Their complete analysis, therefore, involves investigation of their physical properties, including density, particle size, and hydraulic behavior, as well as chemical characterization of their functional groups. In addition, the interdependence of their chemical and physical properties is such that adequate evaluation of their applicability in certain processes can only be obtained by performance tests under simulated operating conditions.

The physical tests used for ion-exchange polymers are generally applicable to both organic and inorganic networks containing all manner of functional groups. Some chemical tests are equally universally applicable with respect to technique, but require variation of the reagents according to the anionic or cationic character of the functional group. Other tests are limited in applicability to a single type of polymer. In selecting the material to be included in this chapter an attempt has been made to include the tests of universal application as well as a limited number of commonly used specific tests. In many cases there is no single method used by all workers to determine a given property. Where this is the situation, the method selected reflects the experience of the authors. Therefore, the inclusion or exclusion of an analytical technique should not in itself be taken as a criterion of superiority of one method over another. The American Society for Testing Materials (ASTM), the Industrial Water Conditioning Institute, and the American Water Works Association (AWWA) have committees working on test procedures for ion-exchange materials. Therefore, it is to be anticipated that in the future their efforts will result in the standardization of methods for the study of ion-exchange resins.

SAMPLING

As in any situation where a non-homogeneous material is being analyzed, the value of the analytical results obtained from a given sample of ion-exchange material depends greatly on the care exercised in obtaining a representative sample. In the case of unused material the sampling problem is the same as that for other granular materials in that one must either be certain that the material to be sampled is well mixed by a tumbling process prior to sampling; or, in cases where the volume of material is too great, that a sufficient number of small samples are taken, combined and mixed to form a representative sample.

PRETREATMENT OF THE SAMPLE

All the properties of an ion-exchange material are affected to some degree by the ionic form of the functional groups. For this reason, it is usually advisable to convert the sample to some known ionic form or "standard state" prior to analysis. Unfortunately for the case of used material, the procedures used for converting the sample to a standard state frequently effect a general "clean-up" of the sample at the same time. Therefore, if the "as is" performance of a given material is to be studied, the sample for analysis is best drawn after regeneration of the entire bed of material in the unit in which it is being operated. Such samples would then be analyzed without any further pretreatment. Subsequent to the initial performance analysis they may, if desired, be converted to a standard ionic state and reanalyzed so that a more rigorous comparison of their present chemical properties with their original properties may be made.

Pretreatment of Cation-Exchange Materials

In the majority of cases cation-exchange materials are regenerated to either the sodium (with salt or alkali) or the hydrogen form (with acid) in cyclic processes. Furthermore, they are almost universally sold in these two forms. For this reason either the hydrogen or the sodium form is to be preferred as the standard state. Where the material has been used, it is preferable to regenerate it to the hydrogen form, since the replacement of most cations by hydrogen ion is more easily accomplished than their replacement with sodium. Further, the hydrogen form of the resin is required for the testing of the chemical characteristics of the material. If analysis based on the sodium form of the resin is desired, used material should be converted first to the hydrogen form and subsequently to the sodium form.

Pretreatment of Anion-Exchange Materials

Anion-exchange materials are usually used in the hydroxide or free-amine form. However, they are most commonly sold in the chloride form. Further, the hydroxide form of the majority of anion-exchange materials is not stable to oven-drying. Since the chloride form is convenient for most analyses and is stable to drying, it is generally taken as the standard state for anion-exchange materials except for weakly basic structures, which are generally sold in the free-amine form and are stable to drying in this state. Since their chloride forms are not easily rinsed without hydrolysis, the free-amine form is frequently used as the standard state.

PHYSICAL PROPERTIES

Ion-exchange polymers are customarily produced and used in the form of granular or spherical particles. In special applications these particles may vary from material retained on 16 mesh (1.2 mm diameter) to material passing through 325 mesh (0.044 mm diameter). In the average cyclic processes, however, particles range from 16 to 50 mesh (1.2 to 0.3 mm diameter). Since the major portion of the applications of these materials involves their use in very dilute aqueous solutions, the physical properties of the fully hydrated polymer are most commonly measured. Further, since these materials are usually used in column operations, measurement of hydraulic properties in such operations is included.

All physical properties are dependent to some degree on the chemical form of the functional group. Although it is sometimes desirable to determine the properties on an "as is" basis, it is more usual to convert the resin to a known ionic form before making any physical measurements. The properties of cation exchangers are usually measured with the functional groups in either the sodium or hydrogen form; anion exchangers are evaluated most frequently in either the chloride or hydroxide forms. These standard forms are selected because they are the ones in which most resins are sold and also because they represent the common regenerated forms for commercial applications. In cases where the resin is regenerated to other ionic forms the physical properties may be more profitably determined on that regenerated form.

Screen Analysis

The method selected for screen analysis of ion-exchange resins is a function of the particle size of the resin to be

screened and the use for which the resin is intended. Where
the majority of the resin sample is retained on 100-mesh
screens and the resin is to be used in aqueous systems a
wet screening of the desired ionic form is to be preferred.
Samples finer than 100 mesh, on the other hand, are more
conveniently screened air- or oven-dried. In cases where
dry-screening techniques are used, the fact that the majority
of resins swell on hydration must be recognized. The methods
employed are identical to those employed for sands, gravel,
coal, etc. Normally one chooses 8-in. diameter screens of
No. 16, 20, 30, 40, 50, 60, 70 and 100 U.S. screen sizes
as a nest through which the sample is screened, and the
amount retained by each screen is measured.

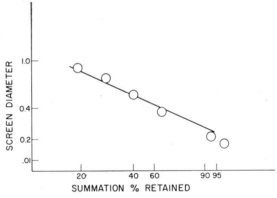

Figure 4.1. Screen analysis plot.

The screen analysis data are used to calculate the effective size and the uniformity of the sample. From the volume
(or weight) of resin per screen cut and the total volume of
all the cuts, the per cent of the sample in each screen cut
and the cumulative per cent are calculated. Typical results
are shown in Table 4.1. Using these results, a plot of cumu-

lative per cent retained as a function of the screen opening in millimeters is made on normal probability paper. (Figure 4.1.)

TABLE 4.1. TYPICAL SCREEN ANALYSIS DATA

Screen Size (U. S.)		Screen Opening (mm)	Volume Resin (ml)	% Resin	Cumulative %
Retained on	16	1.19	0.5	0.24	0.24
	20	0.84	4.6	2.2	2.4
	30	0.59	37.6	18.0	20.4
	40	0.42	89.2	42.7	63.1
	50	0.30	61.7	29.5	92.6
	60	0.25	8.6	4.1	96.7
	70	0.21	5.0	2.4	99.1
	100	0.15	1.5	0.72	99.8
Passing	100		0.2	0.09	99.9

The best straight line is drawn through the points, giving greater weight to the points representing the largest resin fractions. From this line the effective size, which is the screen opening that will retain 90 per cent of the sample, is determined. From the data in Fig. 4.1 the effective size would be 0.34 mm. The mesh size retaining 40 per cent of the sample is also noted. From these two values the uniformity, which is equal to:

$$\frac{\text{Mesh size (mm) retaining } 40\% \text{ of the sample}}{\text{Mesh size (mm) retaining } 90\% \text{ of the sample}}$$

is calculated. In the illustrative example this would be

$$\frac{0.51}{0.34} \text{ or } 1.50$$

Attrition Resistance

The quantitative estimation of the physical stability of ion-exchange polymers to prolonged or repeated exposure to aggressive conditions proves to be one of the most difficult experimental problems. As these materials are intended to be attrition-resistant, the amount of change taking place under simulated operating conditions in a reasonable length of time, say one month, is frequently too small to be measured. Hence, one is usually forced to resort to a set of conditions more severe than are encountered in normal operation and to rate the sample being tested according to its resistance in an arbitrary test relative to that of some material whose field performance is known. Ball milling under mild conditions is such a test. In general practice, changes in the effective size of the material are used as a measure of attrition resistance. Increases in the amount of material passing a given mesh size may also be used. If the sample being studied is in bead form, the decrease in its whole bead content may also be used as an indication of its attrition resistance.

Chemical Attrition

Chemical attrition of ion-exchange polymers may result from the repeated swelling and deswelling of these polymers accompanying the process of their conversion from one ionic form to another, or from actual chemical attack on the polymer backbone. In some cases the tendency to such breakdown may be apparent in a single cycle, while in others it will be noticed only after prolonged exposure to aggressive reagents. Further, knowledge of the attrition resistance of a polymer when cycled with a given set of reagents does not give one more than a license to speculate about its behavior in other systems. It is, therefore, not possible to set up a single procedure for evaluating stability to chemical attrition. This is best done, in the particular case, by alternative treatment of the polymer with the exhaustant and regenerant of the system in which the polymer is to be used.

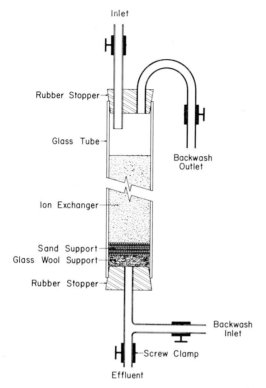

Figure 4.2. Laboratory ion-exchange column.

For example, an anion exchange resin might be studied by alternate treatments with sodium hydroxide and sulfuric acid, using in each case a sufficient volume of acid and alkali to convert the resin from one ionic form to another. With glass column apparatus such as is shown in Figure 4.2, cycles of acid, water, alkali, water, acid, etc. are conducted automatically on a time cycle. A polymer sample of known screen analysis and whole bead content is inserted in the glass tubes, which are fitted with screening at both ends to prevent loss of material. After the desired number of cycles, the material is reconverted to the original ionic form and the size and whole bead content are redetermined. Microscopic examination is also made. Results are calculated in the same manner as those from physical attrition tests. The chemical properties such as moisture and exchange capacity are frequently checked after these cycling tests to obtain information concerning the stability of the functional groups of the polymer to chemical attack.

Density

Three types of density measurements are made on ion-exchange materials. Most common of these is the apparent density or column density in which the pounds of fully hydrated sample per cubic foot of settled bed is determined. The figure so obtained is used both in the sale of resin and in the calculation of the charge and performance of commercial units. Of interest in estimating hydraulic properties is the true density of the hydrated swollen polymer, as it is this value that permits the estimation of whether a polymer will float in a given regenerant or whether two polymers will separate in a mixed bed system. A third measurement of theoretical interest to the polymer chemist is the true polymer density in the particular solvent to be used.

Void Volume

The void volume, or that per cent of a backwashed and settled bed that is not occupied by hydrated resin particles, may be calculated from the apparent density and the true wet density by the following formula:

Let

D_T = true density of hydrated polymer in g/ml

D_A = apparent density of hydrated polymer in g/ml

then

$\dfrac{D_A}{D_T}$ = volume occupied by resin in each ml of settled bed

$\left(1 - \dfrac{D_A}{D_T}\right)$ 100 = per cent voids

For maximum accuracy the actual density of water at the temperature at which the other densities are measured should be substituted for the one in this equation.

In cases where the values of the true wet density and the apparent density are not known, an estimate of the void volume may be made by simply draining a small bed of resin and measuring the volume of liquid that drains off. This is, of course, subject to the uncertainty of the completeness with which the water is removed from the resin.

Hydraulic Properties

The behavior of granular ion-exchange materials in a flowing system must be determined to permit designing of the units in which they are operated. In particular, knowledge of the pressure drop and backwash characteristics as a function of flow rate and temperature is essential to determine whether a particular unit will permit the desired rate of flow and whether the bed may be properly backwashed between cycles. Since ion-exchange materials are commonly used in dilute aqueous solutions, their hydraulic properties are usually determined in water. Where major changes in polymer density occur between ionic forms, the pressure drop is usually determined on the regenerated form of the resin and the backwash characteristics on the exhausted form.

Pressure Drop

The pressure drop through a bed of ion-exchange material is a function of the particle size and shape, of the true hydrated density of the particle, and of the temperature and rate of flow of the liquid passing through the column. In the study of a particular polymer, however, it is customary to measure the pressure drop through a representative classified polymer bed as a function of flow rate at the temperature at which the bed is to be operated.

The pressure drop per foot of bed is obtained simply by dividing the measured pressure differential by the measured bedheight. However, since it is frequently difficult to control the temperature of the water used in these experiments, small temperature differences may be corrected to a constant temperature by multiplying the observed pressure drop by the ratio of the viscosity of water at the desired temperatures to the viscosity at the actual temperature of measurement.

Bed Expansion

The expansion of a bed of an ion-exchange material when liquid is passed through it upflow is, like the downflow pressure drop, a function of the particle size and shape, the true density and the temperature and rate of flow of the liquid passing through it. Again, as in the case of pressure drop, the bed expansion is a function of the flow rate of water through the bed at one or more temperatures. The same apparatus used for pressure drop experiments may be used for measuring bed expansion:

$$\frac{(\text{height expanded bed} - \text{original bed height})\ 100}{\text{original bed height}} = \%\ \text{bed expansion}$$

Results are expressed in terms of temperature and flow rates. As in the case of pressure drop, small temperature fluctuations can be corrected by multiplying the expansion by the ratios of the viscosities of water at the desired temperature and the temperature of measurement.

Swelling

Volume changes in ion-exchange materials frequently accompany conversion of the polymer from one ionic form to another, or the change of solvents of differing ionic strengths or dielectric properties. As in the case of chemical attrition, the possible number of variables is so large that the investigator is wise to limit himself to the particular system in which he plans to work. The procedure used in all cases is similar. The sample is first converted to one of the ionic forms and its volume is carefully measured by the same procedure used in measuring column densities. This sample is then converted to the second ionic form and the volume is remeasured. The same general procedure is followed in determining the volume change resulting from a change in solvents. The volume of the resin swollen with the first solvent is first measured; the first solvent is displaced by the second and the volume of the sample is remeasured.

Solubility

One of the necessary requirements of an ion-exchange polymer is that it be insoluble. However, in some cases ion-exchange materials contain low molecular weight residues that give rise to apparent solubility. It is the concentration of this latter material rather than polymer solubility that is usually measured in most solubility determinations.

Aesthetic Properties

Since ion-exchange polymers are in some cases used to treat water intended for domestic use, the aesthetic properties of color, odor and taste are frequently estimated. In the case of color and odor both that of the resin itself and of the aqueous phase in contact with the resin are measured. Taste, of course, is primarily concerned with the extract, except in the special case, not treated herein, where the polymers themselves are used as internal medicines.

Color. As yet no standard method for rating the color of ion-exchange materials has been proposed. Where color is measured, arbitrary standards have been selected representing the normal range of colors for such materials. On the other hand, a large number of procedures have been proposed for the determination of the color of the aqueous phase (color "throw") that has been in contact with the resin. These methods vary principally in the ratio of water to resin and in the pretreatment of the resin.

Odor. An estimation of the odor of water treated with ion-exchange resins may be made by applying the standard APHA method for odor to the effluent. Odor of the resin itself is likewise a somewhat qualitative value. In extreme cases it is detectable simply by sniffing the container in which the resin is stored. In others some warming technique is required.

Taste. Taste tests, when used for ion-exchange resins, refer to the taste of the water in contact with the resin. This test may also be run on the effluent. It is usually run only if the effluent is odorless and neutral. As in the case of odor tests, the results are dependent upon the sensitivity of the observer.

CHEMICAL PROPERTIES

The chemical properties of an exchange resin are determined both by the nature skeletal backbone (styrene-divinylbenzene, phenol-formaldehyde, acrylic-divinylbenzene, etc.) and by the nature of the functional group ($-SO_3H$,

$-COOH$, $-NH_2$). To a large degree, the functional group determines the nature of the exchange equilibria and the skeletal structure, the stability of the resin.

Moisture-Holding Capacity

The moisture-holding capacity of an ion-exchange polymer is frequently used as a rough means of estimating the effective cross-linking of the polymer. Like all other chemical properties of these materials, the hydration is dependent upon the nature of the functional group and upon its ionic form. For a given group and form, however, a reduction in the amount of cross-linking agent in the polymer will bring about an increase in the hydration.

Since hydration is dependent on ionic form, pretreatment of the sample to a known form is particularly important. Further, ample time for soaking the sample in water prior to the measurement of solids content and carefully controlled drainage conditions must be provided.

In general, cation-exchange polymers may be dried (110° C) in any ionic form. However, many anion-exchange polymers, particularly those containing quaternary structures, are subject to degradation when dried in the hydroxide form. Therefore, the solids content of this form, when required, must be obtained by indirect methods wherein a weight of wet hydroxide form is converted to a stable salt form, dried, and the dry weight of the hydroxide form obtained by calculation based upon the capacity and equivalent weights of the ions.

While the oven-dried (110°C) weight of the sample is the value most frequently measured, in some cases where fouling by inorganic constituents (silica, iron, heavy metals) is suspected, an ignited ash content may be of value. In this case the sample is usually analyzed "as is" as well as after the anticipated special regeneration procedure rather than after the usual conditioning procedures aimed at converting the sample to a known ionic form.

Characterization of Functional Groups

The nature of the functional group of an ion-exchange material may be ascertained by means of the equilibrium titration curve, which provides a means of accurately characterizing the acid-base properties of the functional group as well as of determining the exchange capacity of the material. The method is analogous to that used for soluble acids and bases. It is, however, a time-consuming process and is recommended only for research situations. Successful characterization of non-functional cationic materials has been obtained by an abbreviated procedure by which dissociation constant of materials of known capacity is obtained.

In some cases where the functional group of the polymer is highly dissociated in either the hydrogen or hydroxide form, the titration curve may be determined by direct titration. Even here, however, it is usually necessary to grind the polymer to increase the rate at which equilibrium is attained and a slow establishment of equilibrium between solid and solution is still noted at the end point. More accurate measurements are obtained by a method wherein a series of samples of known content of functional group are equilibrated with varying known amounts of acid or alkali. The equilibrium pH is then determined and a plot of pH *vs* milliequivalents of acid or base added is made. Typical titration curves of conventional ion-exchange resins are shown in Figures 2.2 and 2.3 (pp. 14-15). The curves in these figures have been plotted in such a manner as to illustrate how titration curves may be employed for the purpose of determining both the acidity or basicity and the exchange capacity of an ion exchanger.

Total Capacity Measurements

In routine work, ion-exchange materials are most rapidly characterized by the measurement of the total numbers of functional groups capable of exchanging ions. This value, expressed as milliequivalents of exchangeable ion per dry gram of polymer, is commonly referred to as the cation or anion exchange capacity of cation and anion exchanging polymers, respectively. In addition to measurement of the total number of groups it is possible to characterize them further as weakly or strongly dissociated acids and bases.

Although determination of the total exchange capacity may appear to be simple, many factors complicate it, such as low rates of exchange and diffusion, unfavorable exchange equilibria between certain pairs of ions, inaccessibility of certain exchange sites, and instability of certain ion-exchange polymers. Further, one has the primary problem of converting the sample to some known ionic form prior to analysis. All the determinations below presume that the sample has been given pretreatment to a known ionic form prior to weighing or that the sample is being analyzed on an "as is" basis.

Cation-Exchange Capacity

The number of groups capable of exchanging cations is conveniently determined by converting the resin groups to the hydrogen form with an excess of acid, rinsing to remove this excess acid, and equilibrating the resin with a known excess of standard sodium hydroxide. Hydrochloric acid is recommended for the conversion of the resin to the hydrogen form except in cases involving certain heavy metal forms of cation exchangers that precipitate with chloride of sulfate ions. In such cases, nitric acid is employed. The resin is usually converted to the acid form before weighing to eliminate errors arising from differences in the equivalent weights of different ionic forms. However, the sodium, or other known ionic form may be used as a weighing form, followed by conversion of the weighed sample to the hydrogen form. The use of deionized or distilled water in the rinse step is important because many resins are capable of exchanging hydrogen ions for the cations in tap water, thereby giving rise to long rinses and low capacities. Sodium chloride is added to the standard sodium hydroxide to drive the exchange equilibrium for weakly acidic exchangers to completion.

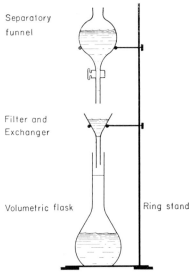

Separatory
funnel

Filter and
Exchanger

Volumetric flask

Ring stand

Figure 4.3. Apparatus for measuring exchange capacity.

Highly Dissociated Cationic Groups. In many instances wherein the characterization of ion-exchange polymers is attempted, a differentiation between cation-exchanging groups whose hydrogen forms are ionic and those whose hydrogen forms are largely undissociated is desired. The capacity determination outlined measures the sum of both weakly and strongly dissociated groups. A clear-cut differentiation between the two types of groups can only be obtained when they vary greatly in their degree of ionization, but an estimation of the number of highly dissociated groups may be obtained by taking advantage of the equilibrium reaction:

$$\text{Resin H} + \text{Na}^+ \rightleftharpoons \text{Resin Na} + \text{H}^+$$

This reaction may be driven toward completion to the right by a large excess of sodium ions if Resin H is highly ionized. Under the same conditions the extent of reaction of weakly acidic groups, such as a carboxyl group, is 0 to 10 per cent depending on their acid strength. Thus, if the polymer is converted to the hydrogen form, rinsed free of excess acid, and eluted with a neutral salt such as sodium chloride or sodium sulfate, the fraction of the hydrogen ions eluted will be proportional to the degree of ionization of the polymer groups (Figure 4.3).

Anion-Exchange Capacity

The anion-exchange capacity can be determined by converting the resin to the hydroxide form, rinsing free of excess hydroxide, and subsequently equilibrating the resin with an excess of standard acid in a manner analogous to that used in the determination of cation-exchange capacity. However, inaccuracies arise from the drying of the hydroxide form of some anion exchange resin in the solids determination and from the introduction of carbonate in the preparation and rinsing of the resin. Further, with quaternary resins, the conversion of the material to the hydroxide form is not easily accomplished when the resin to be analyzed is in a variety of ionic forms.

In a more widely applicable method the sample is converted to the chloride form with hydrochloric acid rinsed with alcohol to remove the excess chloride while preventing hydrolysis of weakly basic chlorides, and subsequently eluted with an excess of sodium sulfate to permit determination of total chloride. This method may be modified to permit the differentiation between weakly and strongly dissociated bases by eluting first with a liter of $0.15M$ ammonia followed by sodium sulfate. The capacity calculated from the titer of the ammonia solution approximates the weakly basic capacity of the polymer and that calculated from the titer of the sodium sulfate leach the strongly basic capacity of the resin. The total anion-exchange capacity is the sum of the two capacities. This value of the total anion capacity is usually 2 to 3 per cent higher than that obtained by a single leaching with sodium sulfate.

A further modification of this method for routine analysis involving materials known to contain only quaternary nitrogen involves the use of water instead of alcohol for the wash step. This method, which gives total capacity measurements identical with the alcohol wash for this class of compounds has the natural advantage of conservation of reagents.

Performance Tests

Basically, the performance of any reactant of a simple, homogeneous chemical system should be predictable from the equilibrium and rate constants. Although the nature of ion-exchange resins polymers is such that one cannot predict quantitatively their performance from simple equilibrium and kinetic measurements, such measurements are of considerable importance for comparative and qualitative considerations. Until our basic understanding of the nature of the equilibrium and kinetics of ion exchange is enhanced, the quantitative aspects of ion exchange can be described only by performance tests under actual operating conditions. However, certain equilibrium and rate measurements will be described because of their value for comparing resins on a relative basis.

Batch Methods

The comparison of various ion-exchange resins with respect to their relative equilibrium and kinetic behavior can be performed by batch techniques, i.e., by following the change in composition of an electrolyte solution in contact with an ion-exchange resin. The kinetic behavior may be approximated by observing the change in composition of the solution as a function of time. The equilibrium constant of exchange or the selectivity coefficient may be approximated from the ionic composition of the resin and solution phase after the equilibrium has been established.

Selectivity and Equilibrium Measurements

A sample of resin containing approximately two milli-equivalents of exchangeable ions in the desired ionic form is placed in a 250-ml stoppered flask containing 50 ml of a $0.1N$ aqueous solution. The flask is shaken overnight. The resin is then separated from the solution by decantation or filtration and washed with 100 ml of deionized water. The resin and solution (plus washings) are analyzed for each of the two ions that are involved in the exchange process.

The selectivity coefficient, K_D, for the exchange,

$$R - M_1 + M_2 \rightleftharpoons R - M_2 + M_1,$$

is calculated from the equation,

$$K_D = \left[\frac{M_2}{M_1} \right]_R \times \left[\frac{M_1}{M_2} \right]_S$$

where

R represents the resin phase,

S represents the solution phase,

M_1 and M_2 represent the monovalent ions undergoing exchange.

Since K_D is not the true thermodynamic equilibrium constant, comparisons of selectivity data should be made at the same ionic strength of the solution phase and at the same equivalent ionic resin compositions. In order that comparisons of selectivity data can be made at equal ionic resin compositions, several equilibrations should be made with solutions of varying $\dfrac{M_1}{M_2}$ ratios and the K_D's are then compared at equivalent $\left(\dfrac{M_1}{M_2}\right)_R$ ratios.

Kinetic Measurements

Although there are several techniques for comparing the kinetic behavior of ion-exchange resins, the simplest method is to follow the change in concentration of a solution that is continuously contacting the resin in a batch agitation system.

Ten milliequivalents of the fully hydrated resin (acid form of cation or base form of the anion-exchange resin) is placed in a 500 ml three-neck, round bottom flask fitted with a stirrer, thermometer, and pipet sampling device. Two hundred and fifty ml of $0.1N$ NaOH (for cation-exchange resins) or $0.1N$ HCl (for anion-exchange resins) is poured into the flask and the agitation started at 400 rpm. At intervals of 30 sec, 1 min, 5 min, 30 min, 1 hr, and 8 hr, 5-ml samples of liquid are withdrawn and titrated. A measure of the relative rates of resins may be determined by plotting the fraction of the total capacity neutralized as a function of the square root of the time and measuring the slope of the line.

Column Testing

Ion-exchange materials are frequently tested for performance in a given application by small-scale column tests.

TABLE 4.2. TYPICAL COLUMN OPERATING EXPERIMENTS

Type of Analysis	Type of Exchanger	Regenerant Solution	Regenerant Level	Test Solution [a]	Breakthrough Test
Acid removal	Weak base	2% Na_2CO_3	6 lb/cu ft	250 ppm HCl-	pH = 4.0
	Quaternary base	4% NaOH	3 and 6 lb/cu ft	250 ppm H_2SO_4	or 20,000 ohm-cm
Salt splitting	Quaternary base	4% NaOH	3 and 6 lb/cu ft	500 ppm NaCl	5% leakage by titration[b]
Salt splitting	Strong acid	5% H_2SO_4	5 and 10 lb/cu ft	500 ppm NaCl	5% leakage by titration
Softening	Strong acid	10% NaCl	7 and 14 lb/cu ft	250 ppm $CaCl_2$- 250 ppm $MgCl_2$	5 ppm leakage
Silica removal	Quaternary base	4% NaOH	4 and 6 lb/cu ft	200 ppm HCl- 20 ppm SiO_2	0.1 ppm SiO_2 leakage

[a] All concentrations as ppm $CaCO_3$ except SiO_2.
[b] Aliquots of the effluent are titrated for acid or base.

The variations of possible test solutions used in this operation are without number, but the method of operation is similar in all cases. Most tests of this type are run in 1- or possibly 2-in. diameter glass columns with a 2-ft depth of sample. The tests usually consist of a conditioning cycle involving a regeneration with a large excess of regenerant solution, followed by exhaustion of the bed with a test solution of known composition. This is followed by one or more cycles of regeneration and exhaustion simulating the conditions under which the sample is to be used. Some of the more commonly used tests are summarized in Table 4.2. The procedure below is a general one which is applicable to any test devised.

An apparatus for such studies may be devised by fitting a one inch internal diameter glass column which is at least five feet long with a suitable bottom closing which is in turn fitted with a side arm outlet (see Figure 4.2). A piece of glass pipe with a rubber stopper fitted with a T-tube makes the simplest form of this apparatus. More sophisticated forms are available commercially. The top of the pipe is similarly fitted with a stopper provided with a side arm inlet tube. This apparatus should be carefully and firmly mounted in an exactly vertical position.

This side arm of the outlet tube is connected to a backwash water supply. This, as well as all other inlets and outlets should be provided with clamps or other rate-regulating devices. Rubber tubing fitted with screw clamps is the simplest regulating device available.

5. GENERAL PRINCIPLES OF ION-EXCHANGE APPLICATIONS*

Ion-exchange substances function to perform several different types of operations, among which are:

(1) transformation of ionic species
(2) removal of ions
(3) concentration of ions
(4) fractionation of mixtures
(5) catalysis

These functions are simply an outgrowth of the ability of an ion exchanger to exchange ions between fixed functional groups in the exchanger and a liquid phase in contact with the resin.

The five categories into which we have divided ion-exchange applications are rather arbitrary, e.g., an operation which is designed to remove ions may also concentrate them. We have classed many of the operations noted on the basis of the particular (major) aim of the process. This brief and elementary chapter is not designed to be all-encompassing. Instead, an attempt has been made to show the versatility of ion exchange by noting a variety of different types of applications. Also a brief comparison of the several techniques of operation is included with a brief discussion of their advantages or conveniences.

---

* This chapter was written in cooperation with Dr. Norman Frisch of the Rohm & Haas Co.

TRANSFORMATION OF IONIC SPECIES

A major application of ion exchange is the replacement of one ionic species by another, often with the idea of replacing a deleterious ion with an innocuous one. Ion-exchange methods often help avoid lengthy precipitation techniques. In some cases the desired product may not be stable and preparation, just before use, may be performed simply by ion-exchange techniques.

The softening of water, during which calcium, magnesium, and other divalent ions are replaced by sodium ions, using a cation exchanger, is an example of the removal of undesirable Ca and Mg ions, and replacement by nonscale-forming Na ions. This is a simple, efficient, inexpensive and compact method of performing the softening operation. The divalent ions to be removed are much more selectively adsorbed than sodium ions; consequently low leakage of these ions results under most operating conditions. Regeneration with NaCl is successful, since the equilibrium relationship between univalent ions and divalent ions is dependent upon total concentration of ions in solution. In concentrated solution the exchanger becomes less selective for divalent ions over the monovalent sodium ion. In fact, at about 30 per cent NaCl, the exchanger does not show any selectivity (the equivalent fraction of Na in solution is the same as the equivalent fraction in the exchanger).

We note that the conversion of K salt to Na salt is rather easily accomplished by ion exchange since the cation exchanger, particularly the strongly acidic sulfonic acid resin, will exhibit a higher affinity for K. This operation is used in wines to convert potassium bitartrate, which is slightly soluble, to the soluble sodium salt, thereby eliminating the chilling operation normally employed. Should the need arise to perform the opposite transformation, ion-exchange resins are also useful. Here, a two-step operation is required. First the Na salt is passed through a strong acid resin in the H form. Complete removal of Na occurs due to the greater affinity of the exchanger for Na. Then the acid solution is best neutralized with KOH. Should no dilution be desirable, the acid solution could rather be passed through a weak acid resin in the K form.

A limitation of a simple exchange of one ion for another by ion exchange is that the ion to be replaced be more selectively adsorbed by the resin. If we had attempted to replace K in the resin by Na in solution, even at very slow flow rates we would only be able to utilize a slight portion of the normal column capacity of the resin. Similarly, the favorable exchange occurs to an effective (100 per cent removal) capacity. We can increase this capacity until it is identical with the volume capacity of the resin by reducing the flow rate and also the particle size. Usually the economic balance precludes more than 75 to 90 per cent utilization of exchange capacity.

Advantages which stem from the ion-exchange conversion technique include the high purity of the product (no by-products), and also high recovery. One restriction on the use of this technique is the necessity for using relatively dilute solutions; otherwise leakage of the undesirable ion will occur even in cases in which high selectivity for this ion exists. Dilution of the salt solutions, followed by exchange and concentrations via evaporation, may be required in the treatment of strong salt solutions.

Other applications of this technique include the analytical method used for the determination of the total salt concentration of a solution. By converting all cations to hydrogen ions, a simple titration permits easy evaluation of total concentration.

REMOVAL OF IONS

From the definition of ion exchange we require the substitution of one ion for another. One of the most important uses of ion exchange is the complete removal of ions from solution. This may occur by the replacement of cations by H^+, and the replacement of anions by OH^-; the product is H_2O, a product virtually un-ionized. This topic will be discussed in detail in the water-conditioning chapter. It should be noted that the operation can be conducted in several ways: (1) by passing solution first through a strongly acidic (sulfonic) cation resin in the hydrogen form and then through the anion resin in the hydroxyl form; (2) by passing solution through a strong base resin in the hydroxyl form and then through a cation exchanger in the hydrogen form; and (3) by passing the solution through a mixture of the two resins. The degree of salt removal required and the stability and solubility of the main constituents in acidic or basic solution determine the method of treatment.

In addition to deionizing water, soluble polymers may be treated to remove traces of salt whose presence may yield poor polymer properties (excessive electrical conductivity, etc.). Similarly, both deashing and partial decolorization of raw sugar solutions can be accomplished. In a simple case the undesirable component exists as an acid or base and removal requires only treatment with a single resin (formic acid removal from formaldehyde).

In addition to typical ion-exchange phenomena, removal of complex color bodies, high molecular weight structures such as tannins, polyphenols, etc., may be accomplished on one of the several weakly basic porous exchangers. In many cases this does not appear to be an ion-exchange phenomenon, as these acids are too weak to be exchanged by weakly basic resins of the polyamine type. It appears that an adsorption phenomenon is operating. Here the large surface area in conjunction with the polar surface groups results in the removal of all but the last traces of many color bodies. Regeneration with caustic completes the cycle. A similar phenomenon occurs with quaternary resins, such as IRA-401, in the presence of phenols. Unfortunately the adsorptive binding is so strong that special techniques, such as desorption in methanol or oxidative attack of the phenol, is necessary to regenerate the resin.

Several interesting methods for the removal of salts from water, i.e., for the desalting of sea water, depend upon properties of ion-exchange resins. The first method, useful only for emergencies, consists of a silver form of ion-exchange resin which is mixed with barium hydroxide. When sea water is percolated through the mixture the following reactions take place:

$$NaCl + AgR \rightarrow NaR + AgCl \downarrow$$
$$MgSO_4 + Ba(OH)_2 \rightarrow Mg(OH)_2 \downarrow + BaSO_4 \downarrow$$

Thus the major components of sea water are removed.

Another desalting process which has been commercialized depends upon the ion exclusion properties of resins. In this case, the "permselective" ion-exchange membranes described in a previous chapter are employed. Migration of ions through these membranes results from the imposition of an electrical potential across the membrane. When the membrane is prepared from cation exchange material it is termed a cation-permeable membrane. Since the cation resin possesses a high concentration of fixed anion groups, only a low concentration of anions can penetrate into the membrane. (When high salt concentrations are used, the membrane suffers a loss of its exclusion ability.) The following diagram shows one method of desalting sea water:

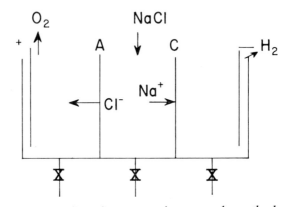

As shown, sodium ions can migrate to the cathode compartment through the cation permeable membrane, while chloride ions are removed through the anion membrane. Little migration occurs from the electrode compartments. A substantial reduction of NaCl concentration in the middle compartment results, with a mixture of NaCl and NaOH in the anodic compartment and NaCl and HCl formed in the cathodic section. In commercial units many cells are arranged in series; thus alternate compartments produce diluted and concentrated salt solutions.

A novel removal method depends upon complex formation. Often commercial grade hydrochloric acid will contain traces of iron which gives it a yellow color and also makes it unsuitable for many uses. Iron (III) exists largely as $FeCl_6^{\equiv}$ in concentrated hydrochloric acid (also in acid more concentrated than $6N$). When this acid is passed through a strongly basic ion-exchange resin in the Cl^- form, the following reaction takes place:

$$3[R-N-(CH_3)_3Cl^-] + FeCl_6^{\equiv} \rightarrow [RN-(CH_3)_3]_3FeCl_6^{\equiv} + 3Cl^-$$

Thus iron is removed and replaced by an equivalent amount of Cl^- (i.e., hydrochloric acid). When iron begins to leak through the bed, acid flow is stopped and regeneration with water is sufficient to remove iron from the bed. (At low acid concentrations, complexing does not occur and iron is washed off the resin quite efficiently.)

CONCENTRATION OF IONS

A major use of ion-exchange resins is the concentration of ions, either for recovery or as a means of pollution reduction. In many analytical schemes designed to determine a particular substance at parts per million levels, pre-concentration of solutions at parts per billion levels by ion exchange is a convenient first step. Naturally elution of the desired ion must utilize a non-interfering eluant which removes the ion quite efficiently.

The value of ion-exchange resins for concentration stems from the ease of reversing the affinity of the resin for a particular ion by changes in the nature of the competing ion, changes in concentration, and changes in pH (acidity or basicity of the solution). In addition, the high capacities of the synthetic exchange resins permit the ions to be stored in a small volume (this is a convenient method when field analyses are to be attempted).

In order to obtain maximum recovery of a given ion during elution (recovery of adsorbed ions), recycling techniques are often used (split elution). Here the last volume of eluant obtained which contains low concentration of eluted ion is recycled after the next run to remove the ion again. By this technique, maximum concentration can be effected.

Among the many applications utilizing ion-exchange resins for concentration purposes, metal recovery is an outstanding one. In many cases, especially in those in which pollution is the major concern, removal of toxic or otherwise undesirable ions from waste streams can be easily accomplished by chemical reaction (addition of alkali, etc.). However, in the plating industry, chromium, which exists largely as Cr (VI) (hexavalent chromium), cannot be removed by pH changes. While reduction with sulfur dioxide (SO_2) is a possible procedure, the precipitated chromium III (trivalent chromium) is contaminated with other trivalent elements and its value is lost. Also subsequent reuse would require re-oxidation of the concentrated chromium to the hexavalent state.

Ion-exchange resins, especially the strongly basic types, serve to remove chromate, either from acidic (pH = 2)* or neutral solutions, at low concentrations (up to 1000 ppm). By eluting with 4 per cent NaOH, a solution of sodium chromate can be obtained. Subsequently, the solution is converted to chromic acid by passage through a styrene divinylbenzene sulfonic acid resin. Thus $CrO_4^=$ pollution is avoided, and a concentration of (usually) 100 to 500 ppm of chromium (CrO_3 basis) to 2 per cent H_2CrO_4 (170 to 34 fold) results, with an appreciable saving in metal value.

A recent development which depends largely on the concentrating ability of ion-exchange resins is the treatment of radioactive wastes. Rather than store tremendous volumes of "hot" solutions, the radioactive elements are removed by ion-exchange resin and eluted (often by nitric acid) to yield a concentrated solution which is stored until it decays to a safe level.

One additional concentration scheme worth mentioning† is the recovery of copper as the ammonium complex. In the spinning of cuprammonium rayon, a "blue water" and a spinning acid are used. Typical concentrations involved are:

	Blue Water, g per liter	Spinning Acid, g per liter
Cu	0.08	8–16
NH_3	0.75	
H_2SO_4		65
pH	10	

---

* At this low pH, chromate exists largely as $HCrO_4^-$.

† Detailed discussion of many hydrometallurgical applications will be found in Chapter 7.

In order to recover copper from these solutions, ion exchange resins are utilized.

$$2RH + Cu(NH_3)_4^{++} \rightleftharpoons RCu(NH_3)_4^{++} + 2H^+$$

The $Cu(NH_3)_4^{++}$ complex is quite strongly adsorbed on cation resins, pushing off the univalent ions present (Na^+, NH_4^+). At full loading, there is evidence which indicates that copper exists as $Cu(NH_3)_2^{++}$ complex.

The regeneration is conducted with spinning acid. When a resin containing weak acid groups is used, the removal of copper (which is selectively bound in the exhaustion stage) is quite efficiently accomplished. Precipitation of copper occurs when the spent regenerant is treated with ammonia to form basic copper sulfate. This is a particularly economical process since regenerant is readily available. The resin is quite selective for copper, and efficient regeneration results from change in pH.

Many other processes take advantage of the concentrating abilities of ion-exchange resins.

FRACTIONATION OF MIXTURES

Two special cases of fractionation depend upon ionic size, and the extent of ionization. Thus, the passage of large ionic species, such as sulfonic acid dyes, with small mineral ions through anion-exchange resins results in preferential removal of the mineral acid. In many cases, exchange of the dye occurs on the surface of the exchange resin only. Even though many of these large structures possess exceptional affinities for ion-exchange resins, they are excluded by virtue of their size. This procedure is useful for desalting high molecular weight dyes (often the salt present was used to "salt" out the dye).

A simple means for the separation of weakly and strongly dissociated acids depends upon the ability of weakly basic resins to react preferentially with strong acids. Thus the passage of a mixture of hydrochloric acid and acetic acid through a bed of weakly basic resin results in some removal of acetic acid. Hydrochloric acid is more strongly bound and acetic acid travels down the column faster and appears in the effluent with little hydrochloric acid. A similar separation is possible with a strongly basic resin, but the nature of this type of resin makes the separation less favorable.

Two general methods useful for separations involve adsorption chromatography and elution chromatography. The former is generally applied to the separation of solutes which exhibit substantially different selectivities for a resin (such as the separation of divalent and univalent ions). By slow passage of a solution containing these ions through a strongly dissociated resin, the ion less tightly bound (univalent) is displaced in a band to the exit end of a column, while the tightly bound ion (divalent) occupies the band extending from the influent end. In some cases a clean-cut separation of bands results, with no interference.

Elution chromatography is applied to separations of closely similar ionic species. Thus, the chloride (Cl^-), bromide (Br^-) and iodide (I^-) ions are rather tightly adsorbed on a strong base anion-exchange resin. By adding a ternary mixture to the top of the resin bed and slowly percolating through a sodium nitrate solution ($NaNO_3$) ($0.5N$), a band of Cl^- will appear in the effluent first, then Br^- and finally a wide band of relatively dilute I^-. Iodide ions are quite strongly adsorbed by the quaternary resin. In order to avoid the slow displacement of I^-, a more concentrated nitrate solution may be used. Instead, it is often convenient to progressively increase the nitrate concentration during the elution step. This is termed gradient elution; by use of simple mixing devices it is possible to increase (linearly or exponentially) the concentration of eluant as a function of time. Thus, tailing is reduced to a minimum and more concentrated solutions are recovered.

Many ion-exchange separations have been performed.

Analytical chemists find use for this method for the separation of organic acids occurring naturally in foods. A typical procedure will involve use of a strongly basic quaternary resin, using nitrate solutions as the eluant (variable concentration) with suitable buffer solutions.

Another difficult separation—the fractionation of amino acids—has been achieved with ion-exchange resins. After exchange on a strongly acidic resin (H form), elution with HCl is used. Acid concentration is increased from 1 to about $4N$ during this stage. Improved separation results from sodium cycle operation and elution with citrate buffers of increasing pH.

A most interesting separation involving ion exchange is the fractionation of the rare earth elements. The rare earth elements are not as uncommon as their name signifies; they are most important in electric arc electrodes and are becoming increasingly important in the metallurgical, catalytic, and atomic energy fields.

The term "rare earths" normally refers to the group of closely related elements, 58 to 71, inclusive. Until the advent of the new ion-exchange resins, they could be separated only by tedious fractional crystallization. The ion-exchange separation depends upon the competition for rare earth ions between a strong acid resin and a complexing agent at a controlled pH. Several procedures have been successfully applied. In one case a mixture of rare earth oxides is dissolved in hydrochloric acid and dumped into the top of the column originally in the hydrogen form. The rare earths are bound at the top of the bed; deionized water serves to displace excess acid through the resin. In order to develop separate bands of rare earths, dilute buffer (0.1 per cent citric acid-ammonium hydroxide, pH = 8) is slowly passed into the bed and distinct bands of rare earths travel down the column, with the heaviest rare earth in front. The principle on which this type of separation is based involves the competition of rare earth ion between the resin sites and the complexing agent (citrate or ethylene diamine tetra-acetic acid). While the rare earths of higher atomic number are less strongly held than lower atomic number earths by cation resins by virtue of their larger hydrated radius, these same rare earths form less dissociated complexes with citrates; this phenomenon depends upon unhydrated atomic diameter. Thus, a small difference in selectivity is enhanced by the use of a complexing agent. Complete separations of macro-quantities of rare earths by means of ion exchange are now a common operation and are being conducted on a commercial basis in large ion-exchange units.

One additional type of separation can be accomplished by application of the ion-exclusion principle. As noted in a previous chapter, ionic substances are largely excluded from strongly dissociated ion-exchange resins of high capacity. By contrast, weak electrolytes and nonelectrolytes usually distribute themselves rather uniformly within and without the bead.

Mixtures of electrolytes (salt) and nonelectrolytes (glycerin, etc.) may therefore be separated by slow passage through a sulfonic acid cation or quaternary anion exchange resin. The salt will pass through the resin bed relatively unimpeded, while glycerin will be retarded as it diffuses into the resin beads (from the water solution into the water gel). By rinsing the bed with water, glycerin of low salt content may be obtained. Appreciable dilution of the nonelectrolyte occurs during the rinse. It is to be noted that this technique is, by nature, most applicable to high salt content solutions, while ion exchange is often restricted to solutions less concentrated than $0.02N$.

CATALYSIS

Many organic reactions are catalyzed by mineral acids or strong bases. From our knowledge of ion exchange we would expect strong electrolyte-resins to behave in a manner quite similar to these acids or bases. These resins are virtually completely dissociated and also possess several advantages over liquids. When acids are used for catalysis, corrosion and contamination are severe problems. Often recovery of catalysts is uneconomical, but neutralization is required and subsequent separation of undesirable salts must be practiced. Also in several cases, strong acids or bases degrade the reactants so that only low yields can be obtained.

Generally, the catalysis process takes place as the reactants diffuse into the swollen gel and the products diffuse from the bead. Normally this is slower than the corresponding homogeneous process; however, there are some cases in which abnormally high catalysis rates may be obtained by use of ion-exchange resins. Generally, the rates are lower with resins than with the homogeneous systems. Higher molecular weight reactants of a homologous series generally react at a slower rate than simple compounds.

A typical reaction is the esterification of oleic acid with butanol. High yields of *n*-butyloleate are obtainable (96 to 99.5 per cent) with infrequent regeneration of the resins. The preparation of invert sirup from sucrose can be conducted commercially by means of the free acid form of a sulfonic acid resin. Normally this is done with soluble acids which must later be neutralized. Filtration of the resin from the reaction mixture is the only after-processing necessary. In some cases it is convenient to use a fixed bed of resin and recirculate the reactants through the bed.

In some applications it has been found that side products are not formed to an appreciable extent when resins are used. However, some complications such as polymerization within the catalyst bead may reduce catalyst life appreciably.

OPERATIONAL TECHNIQUES

Both intermittent and continuous operations are used in ion exchange; the intermittent type includes batch and columnar operation. In batch contact, a method with only slight usefulness, maximum removal (neutralization, etc.) is limited by the equilibrium relationship between resin and solutes. When viscous solutions are being processed or when the equilibria are irreversible (neutralization and Monobed deionization), batch contact may offer some advantages.

Generally, ion-exchange operations are dictated when extreme removal of solute is required. Obviously many contacts with solute-free resin are required. Columnar operation conveniently suffices for complete removal. In equilibrium operation the solution continuously contacts resin free of solute and consequently there is a high driving force for the removal of solute from solution. In order to achieve maximum removal, the resin at the effluent end of the column must be most highly regenerated.

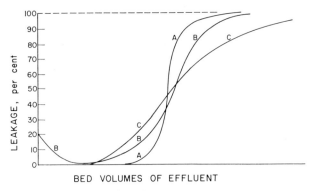

BED VOLUMES OF EFFLUENT

Figure 5.1. Concentration history of ion-exchange column run.

The elements of columnar operation are illustrated in Figures 5.1 and 5.2. Figure 5.1 describes the loading curve or the concentration history of the adsorption phase of columnar operation. Curve A shows the adsorption of an ionic species under conditions of saturation regeneration.

Curve B indicates the adsorption of an ionic species under conditions where leakage is encountered initially due to incomplete elution during the previous cycle. Curve C shows the adsorption of an ion species exhibiting premature breakthrough due to an excessively high flow rate. In Figure 5.2, the second element of the columnar cycle is described, i.e., the elution of the adsorbed ionic species. Curve A shows the elution of adsorbed ionic species under favorable conditions of flow rate and selectivity and Curve B the elution under unfavorable conditions.

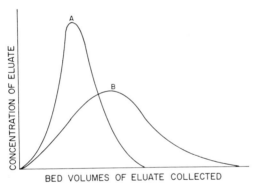

Figure 5.2.   Typical elution curves.

Ordinary concurrent regeneration is not as effective with strongly dissociated resins; consequently, reverse regeneration such as upflow regeneration may be useful. Another useful technique involves air mixing of the regenerated resin to prevent segregation of a band of poorly regenerated resin at the base of a column.

Recently continuous operation of ion-exchange resins has been advocated by some sources. This involves the transfer of resin through regenerating, rinsing and exhaustion zones. Advantages postulated include low inventory of resin and possible tie-in with continuous processing equipment available. Also continuous operation favors concentration operations over removal processes. While some progress has been made in this direction, these complicated devices coupled with attrition losses do not make continuous processing too attractive in most situations today.

6. WATER CONDITIONING*

Natural waters contain varying amounts of dissolved salts and other electrolytes that have been leached from the soil and rocks through and over which the water has passed. Rain water contains traces of electrolytes dissolved from the atmosphere, but the concentration is very low as compared to those encountered in surface and well supplies. The nature of the electrolytes in waters is dependent upon the rocks and soils leached by the waters and therefore the composition of waters throughout the world varies considerably with respect to both concentration and composition.

Water supplies may be divided into two general classes—surface and well. Surface waters are those obtained from rivers, reservoirs, lakes and ponds. These waters are usually not highly mineralized but frequently contain color bodies, turbidity, organic matter, and dissolved gases such as oxygen and carbon dioxide. In some areas where high rates of solar evaporation occur, surface waters may have total dissolved solids approaching the brackish range (1000 to 5000 ppm). The composition of surface waters is frequently dependent on seasonal variations in rainfall and may show marked fluctuations in total dissolved solids.

In midwestern and southwestern areas of the United States, the chief source of water is from deep wells which penetrate the water-bearing strata. These waters are frequently highly mineralized and are pumped from the earth at constant com-

* This chapter was written in cooperation with Mr. F. X. McGarvey of the Rohm & Haas Co.

position free of color and gases. These waters move underground for many miles and reach equilibrium condition with respect to the rock strata. Well waters in the Wisconsin area may have traveled eastward 500 to 1000 miles from the mountain areas of Montana. These waters have been underground for over 500 years.

One of the major applications of ion exchange is to remove salts from waters so that they may be used for boiler feed, laundry, process applications, and for many other purposes. The use of water may be divided into two distinct categories—industrial and domestic.

Before discussing the treatment of these waters by means of ion exchange, it is essential to consider the substances commonly found in water. The most common objectionable substances occurring in water are salts of calcium and magnesium, which impart "hardness," consume soap, and form hard adhering scale on heat-transfer equipment. Calcium and magnesium salts, when their concentrations are combined, are classed as *total hardness,* usually expressed as parts per million (ppm) as $CaCO_3$. These salts produce either *temporary* or *permanent* hardness. Temporary hardness is due to calcium and magnesium bicarbonates. These salts decompose upon heating to yield calcium and magnesium carbonates, and form hard scales in pots and pans as well as in boilers and hot water heaters. The reaction is as follows:

$$Ca(HCO_3)_2 + heat \rightarrow CaCO_3 + CO_2 + H_2O$$

After this reaction occurs, the water and steam will be corrosive and acidic. Permanent hardness is due primarily to sulfates of calcium and magnesium. These salts form scales when their solubility limit is exceeded. Both temporary and permanent hardness are objectionable in boilers where the pH of the boiler water is kept high, since they will precipitate and form scale. All ionized calcium and magnesium salts will consume soap by formation of insoluble salts with the stearic acid in common soaps. A curd will form in the water, rendering the washing operation inefficient.

Sodium and potassium salts are frequently encountered in natural waters. These may be present as chlorides, sulfates, and in rare cases, phosphates and nitrates. Sodium salts are objectionable in high-pressure boilers. When present in high concentration (i.e., greater than 600 ppm) they are noticeable and objectionable in drinking water.

In addition to the major constituents mentioned above, waters also contain varying and usually small amounts (1 to 10 ppm) of silica, iron, manganese and organic matter. These constituents are extremely objectionable even at very low (1 ppm) concentrations. Domestic waters containing iron and manganese are troublesome since small amounts (½ to 1 ppm) cause discoloration of washed clothing, stain porcelain ware, and give rise to taste problems. Silica is a problem in high-pressure boilers since it distills over and deposits scale on the turbine blades; this is extremely difficult and very costly to remove and impairs efficiency of the blades.

One of the major applications of ion exchange is the softening of water. Although there are chemical methods for partially softening water, the ion-exchange method is by far the simplest and cheapest for completely softening water. This process removes calcium and magnesium ions in exchange for equivalent amounts of sodium ions. A cation exchanger is employed and it may be either an inorganic siliceous material or a resin. The process may be represented by the following equations:

$$2RSO_3Na + \begin{Bmatrix} Ca^{++} \\ Mg^{++} \end{Bmatrix} \xrightarrow{\text{Exhaustion}} (RSO_3)_2Ca + 2Na^+ \xrightarrow[\text{Regeneration}]{\text{NaCl}}$$
$$2RSO_3Na + \begin{Bmatrix} Ca^{++} \\ Mg^{++} \end{Bmatrix}$$

In this process, the exchanger is able to remove the calcium and magnesium to a level of below 1 ppm during the exhaustion cycle. Gradually at the end of the run, the hardness starts to appear in the effluent and the endpoint for the run is reached. Normally this point will be set arbitrarily at about 5 ppm. Regeneration is accomplished by washing the bed with a solution of sodium chloride at a 5 to 10 per cent concentration. The regeneration is not 100 per cent efficient and an evaluation of *regeneration efficiency* is required in order to determine the economics involved in the use of the resin. This is done by exhausting the bed and regenerating at different levels with sodium chloride. When the data on capacity, at a particular endpoint, are plotted as a function of amount of regenerant, the resulting curve is called a *loading curve* (Figure 6.1). An *efficiency curve* (Figure 6.2) may be constructed from these data by plotting capacity, which is normally expressed

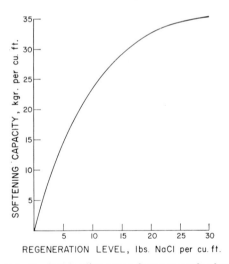

Figure 6.1. Typical loading curve for water softening with a sulfonic acid cation-exchange resin.

as kilograins of calcium carbonate per cubic foot of resin (kgr/cu ft) as a function of pounds salt per kgr hardness removed.

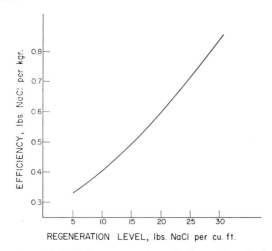

Figure 6.2. Efficiency curve for softening with sulfonic cation-exchange resin.

In addition to the capacity measurement, it is necessary to evaluate the hardness leakage data. Leakage is not due to the inability of the exchanger to remove hardness but to the reversibility of ion-exchange reactions. Ion exchange is carried out normally in a concurrent operation, i.e., all flows, regeneration and exhaustion, are in the same direction, normally downflow. The result of this method is almost complete regeneration of the upper portion of the bed, a certain amount of calcium and magnesium being retained in the lower portion if economy of salt usage is to be attained. The amount of salt necessary to completely regenerate an exhausted bed would be prohibitive economically under most conditions.

The concentration of sodium salts in the water passing

through the upper portion of the bed is equivalent to the total number of cations in the influent. The sodium ions move down the column and exchange to a limited degree with the calcium and magnesium ions in the lower portion. These calcium and magnesium ions are those left on the column from the previous cycle. This results in some leakage of hardness from the bed. The actual amount of leakage is quite small, being only about 1/100 of concentration in the influent. The actual amount is largely dependent upon the sodium ion concentration and the amount of calcium and magnesium left on the bed after regeneration with brine. The leakage may become a large percentage of the influent hardness in waters where the amount of sodium ion is very high. This is particularly true at low regeneration levels (Figure 6.3).

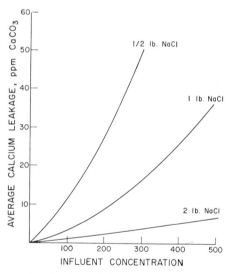

Figure 6.3. Leakage during softening with sulfonic cation-exchange resin.

Various cation-exchange materials are used for softening water by means of ion exchange. In the home, sulfonated polystyrene-based resins and synthetic gel silicates are employed, the resins gradually replacing the less stable and lower-capacity silicates. Although the silicates by virtue of their higher densities have been preferred in home water softening of high iron-bearing waters, techniques have been found which permit one to use resins on such waters. In the field of industrial water softening, both silicates, including the natural greensand, and resins are employed; but here also resins are tending to replace silicates.

The stable polystyrene sulfonic resins have made possible another application of water softening, the "hot zeolite process." In this process most of the hardness is removed from the water by precipitation with lime and soda ash in an enclosed unit at a temperature between 180 and 280°F. The chemicals are added and precipitation occurs according to the following equations:

$$Mg(HCO_3)_2 + Ca(HCO_3)_2 + CaSO_4 + CaO \rightarrow$$
$$CaCO_3 + MgCO_3 + CaSO_4 + \text{some alkalinity}$$

The lime removes only hardness associated with bicarbonate alkalinity. When permanent hardness is present, a slight excess of soda ash is required to precipitate these salts:

$$CaSO_4 + Na_2CO_3 \rightarrow Na_2SO_4 + CaCO_3 + \text{some alkalinity}$$

In practice, the above reactions do not go to completion in the time available in the "contactor" or "activator," and some hardness will remain. Until recently, this hardness was sequestered by polyphosphates. Since the sulfonated styrene-based cation-exchange resins are quite stable under these conditions, softeners are placed in the process after precipitation to remove the residual hardness (usually 20 to 30 ppm) which has passed through the process softener. Because of their instability under these conditions, the inorganic natural and synthetic silicates as well as the phenolic-based resins are unsatisfactory for this application.

Deionization

Another large industrial application of ion exchange is the deionization of waters for boiler feed and other process uses. While softening removes objectionable components, no reduction in total solids is attained and evaporation of the softened water would lead to a massive deposit of salts which is objectionable in high pressure boilers and in other processes.

Deionization is accomplished by first passing the water through a bed of a cation exchanger (sulfonic) which converts all the salts to their corresponding acids. The process follows the equation:

$$RSO_3H + \begin{Bmatrix} NaCl \\ MgSO_4 \\ Ca(HCO_3)_2 \\ SiO_2 \end{Bmatrix} \longrightarrow RSO_3 \begin{Bmatrix} Na \\ Mg \\ Ca \end{Bmatrix} + \begin{Bmatrix} HCl \\ H_2SO_4 \\ H_2CO_3 \\ SiO_2 \end{Bmatrix}$$

The resin is regenerated by the addition of a strong acid, usually sulfuric acid, although hydrochloric acid is used occasionally. The regeneration reaction proceeds according to the equation:

$$RSO_3 \begin{Bmatrix} Na \\ Mg \\ Ca \end{Bmatrix} + H_2SO_4 \longrightarrow RSO_3H + \begin{Bmatrix} Na_2SO_4 \\ MgSO_4 \\ CaSO_4 \end{Bmatrix}$$

This process is very much like the sodium cycle operation and is carried out exactly like the step described previously. Leakage phenomena are similar but greater in magnitude when sodium salts are involved (Figure 6.4). The greatest difficulty experienced in hydrogen cycle operation occurs when sulfuric acid is used to regenerate beds which have been exhausted with large amounts of calcium. This difficulty arises from the insolubility of calcium sulfate in the spent regenerant. If precipitation does occur, the rinse requirements are high and capacity is reduced, because the calcium sulfate, which precipitates as massive crystals, will redissolve and exchange for hydrogen ions on the resin.

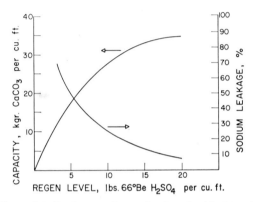

Figure 6.4. Leakage and capacity data for Na-H cycle of a sulfonic cation-exchange resin.

Various methods for avoiding precipitation in the bed have been developed; these involve (a) the use of dilute acid and (b) stepwise regeneration starting with dilute acid and working up gradually to concentrated (5 per cent H_2SO_4). Since regenerant efficiency is rapidly lost at low concentration, the aim of these procedures is to use the highest concentration of acid without risking precipitation within the resin bed.

When large quantities (percentage-wise) of sodium salt are present, the danger of $CaSO_4$ precipitation is greatly reduced, but the problem of "sodium leakage" becomes critical if high quality water is to be obtained. This problem is particularly noticeable at low levels of regeneration. The leakage of sodium ions is a direct result of the low selectivity of the resin for monovalent ions as compared with divalent ions such as the calcium ion. The performance of the exchanger in the hydrogen cycle is a complex function of the regenerant conditions and the water composition.

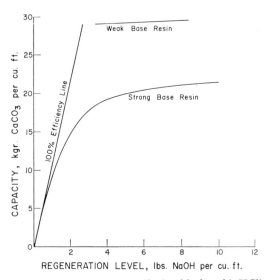

Figure 6.5. Loading curves (hydrochloric acid, HCl) of anion-exchange resins.

After the water has passed through the cation exchanger, the acid must be removed. At this point, a number of choices are available to the user (Figure 6.5). If the quality of effluent need not be great, a weakly basic anion exchanger may be employed. Weak-base anion exchangers will remove strong acids such as HCl, H_2SO_4 and HNO_3. Although some of these exchangers will remove carbon dioxide, they are rarely used for this purpose in industrial installations, since it is more economical to remove the CO_2 by physical means. Degasification may be used for such purposes, and the degasifier is usually located between the cation and anion exchanger. A vacuum degasifier will remove the CO_2 and also reduce the oxygen to a low level. The regeneration of the weak base exchanger is accomplished with slightly more than equivalent amounts of ammonia, soda ash, or caustic.

In some cases of degasification, all the water passes through the hydrogen cycle unit and the pH is adjusted by addition of caustic in the degasification step. It should be pointed out that the solids reduction is proportional to the amount of alkalinity in the water and that the water is usually partially saturated with CO_2, which must be removed by either a vacuum degasifier or stripped by passage through a stream of air.

If the application requires a water of greater purity, the removal of silica and carbon dioxide is a prime factor. The operation of high-pressure steam-turbine generation equipment requires such purity, and for such problems a strongly basic anion exchanger is required. The installation may contain an additional anion-exchange unit, or the whole process may be carried out in a single unit by the mixing of anion and cation exchange resin; the latter method is called mixed bed or Monobed deionization.

The multiple bed system is frequently used for large installations. Such units may also contain a "clean-up" Monobed for any leakage that may occur. The water obtained from this type of plant has very high quality and contains less than 0.01 ppm SiO_2. The various deionization systems are schematically described in Figures 6.6 and 6.7. In some cases, the quality is impaired due to leakage of tannins and humic acids which are too high in molecular weight to be exchanged. In these cases, which are usually found in surface waters, it is necessary to use porous anion-exchange resins, which have a higher capacity for high molecular weight acids.

In many respects, the operation of the strongly basic anion exchange is similar to that of the strongly acidic cation exchangers. They do not regenerate as efficiently as the weakly acidic or basic exchangers and must be checked for leakage when used in *reverse deionization*. Reverse deionization, a process not employed in water conditioning, may be conducted with a strongly basic anion exchange resin placed ahead of the cation exchange system.

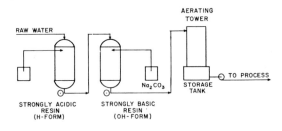

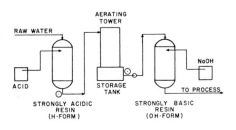

Figure 6.6. Schematic deionization systems.

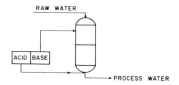

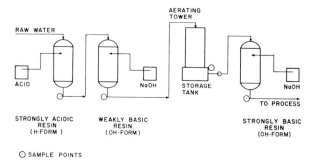

Figure 6.7. Schematic deionization systems.

The role of the strongly basic anion exchangers in deionization is intimately related to the silica problem. Normally for high-pressure boilers, the silica concentration in the boiler must be kept considerably below 1 ppm. This requires that average silica leakage values from a deionization unit must be less than 0.01 ppm for the water used for boiler feed make-up. Silica is a most unusual ion, if an ion at all. Apparently the soluble silica enters the bed as $HSiO_3^-$ or $HSi_2O_3^-$ and after contact with the resin for some time it becomes a polymer having the general formula $(SiO_2)_x \cdot H_2O$. It is necessary to dissolve this precipitate or polymer before it can be removed from the bed during regeneration. In order to obtain an effluent of 0.01 ppm SiO_2 or less, it is necessary to remove the silica completely. This is accomplished by use of warm caustic, long contact time, and careful rinsing. Leakage of cations must be kept at a minimum to obtain an optimum silica capacity.

Some of the silica present in certain water supplies is not in true solution but exists in a colloidal state. Unfortunately, most of this silica is not adsorbed by the anion exchange resin and therefore is not removed during the deionization operation. Where such conditions exist and complete silica removal is essential, the colloidal silica is removed during the water pretreatment operations, which normally consist of coagulation and filtration.

Dealkalization by Anion Exchange

Although we have discussed anion exchangers in their conventional role, which is to remove acids, it should be stated that strongly basic anion exchangers are frequently used in anion interchange reactions to remove alkalinity according to the following equation:

$$RN^+Cl^- + \left\{ \begin{array}{l} NaHCO_3 \\ CaSO_4 \end{array} \right\} \longrightarrow RN^+HCO_3 + \left\{ \begin{array}{l} NaCl \\ CaCl_2 \end{array} \right\}$$

The reaction is reversed by regeneration with an excess of sodium chloride in 5% solution. This process gives no solids reduction but eliminates objectionable alkalinity without the use of acid.

In any discussion of the development of deionization by means of ion-exchange resins, the differences between this method and distillation should be mentioned. Each has its place and in certain instances supplements the other. Ion exchange can be used to remove completely all electrolytes, including weak acids such as silicic acid, boric acid, and phenols. The true nonelectrolytes, however, cannot be removed; therefore one cannot assure sterility and freedom from pyrogens by ion-exchange deionization. On the other hand, several stages of distillation are required to remove electrolytes to the same degree as by ion exchange. Therefore, industries requiring water of high purity, sterile and pyrogen-free, resort to a combination of ion exchange followed by a single-stage distillation.

It is virtually impossible to prepare on any modest scale water that is free of all traces of impurities. This is true for ion exchange as well as for distillation. Contamination from piping, containers, and storage vessels contributes to this problem. Current practices in which ultra-pure water is required call for careful pretreatment of the water supply prior to either distillation or deionization. Such pretreatments include filtration, coagulation, or chlorination. Therefore, the choice between deionization by ion exchange resins or by distillation depends upon many factors, several of which are raw water composition, desired purity or quality of finished water, space requirements, and fuel economics. It is frequent practice to use ion exchange for waters containing less than 600 ppm of total dissolved solids and where sterility and pyrogens are not a problem. However, there are many instances where waters containing more than 1000 ppm are also being treated successfully by ion exchange.

7. ION EXCHANGE IN HYDROMETALLURGY AND RELATED FIELDS*

Another major field of application of ion exchange is hydrometallurgy—the concentration, purification, and recovery of metal values from aqueous solutions. In some instances, the recovered metal has a large monetary value, in others it is an ion that must be removed because of toxicity or some other objectionable feature.

The current and prospective uses of ion exchange in this field can be classified into the following categories:

(1) recovery from ore leach solutions (hydrometallurgy)
(2) recovery from sea water
(3) recovery from waste streams
(4) separations of chemically similar elements

ION EXCHANGE IN HYDROMETALLURGY

Recovery of Uranium

The most important use of ion exchange in hydrometallurgy is the concentration and recovery of uranium from ores. Since the harnessing of nuclear fission, there has been a constant world-wide search for uranium-bearing ores. Of

---

* This chapter was written in cooperation with Dr. Albert Preuss of the Rohm & Haas Co.

the known reserves in the free world, probably 95 per cent of the uranium exists in ores with uranium contents below 0.2 per cent U_3O_8. By the standards of most chemists, this is only a trace impurity. Yet the course of the whole world depends upon extracting uranium from such low-grade ores.

Unfortunately none of the normal means of upgrading ores such as flotation or gravity concentration has proved effective in separating uranium-rich materials from the gangue. The only course left then is to leach the bulk material to produce a fairly low grade uranium leach liquor.

The cheapest acid leaching system utilizes sulfuric acid; hydrochloric and nitric acid would also be effective though economically prohibitive. In some cases, the uranium is present in a reduced state (tetravalent) U^{IV}. Whenever U^{IV} occurs, an oxidant must be added to the leaching system. The two oxidants that are currently being used are MnO_2 (manganese dioxide) and $NaClO_3$ (sodium chlorate).

The leaching of the ground ore is done in a slurry with sulfuric acid. After leaching with agitation, the slurry is then filtered and the cake washed. The resultant leach liquor is usually clarified further by passing the solution through a sand bed or a pre-coat filter. The liquor at this point is extremely clear, with only a few ppm of turbidity at the most.

The leach liquor at this stage contains many dissolved salts as well as uranium. The particular ions present, as well as their range of concentration, will depend primarily on the uranium ore being leached and are enumerated on page 104.

Uranium could be recovered from the above leach liquor by treating the solution with a reducing agent such as powdered iron or aluminum in the presence of excess phosphate ion. The uranium then precipitates as a uranous phosphate. Such a precipitation from a low-grade South African leach liquor would yield a uranium cake with a U_3O_8 content of about 4 per cent. In contrast, the ion-

CHEMICAL ELEMENTS OCCURRING IN SULFURIC ACID LEACH LIQUORS
OF LOW GRADE URANIUM ORES

	g per liter		g per liter
U	0.15-5	Mn^{++}	0-8 g
Fe^{+++}	0-25	Zn^{++}	0-5 g
Fe^{++}	0- 5	Th	< 1 g
Al^{+++}	0-10	SiO_2	< 1 g
Mg^{++}	0- 5	P_2O_5	< 1 g
Ca^{++}	0- 5	As_2O_5	< 1 g
Na^+	0- 5	Se	< 0.5 g
K^+	0- 5	Cl^-	< 0.5 g
Rare earths	< 0.1	HSO_4^- ⎫	5-100 g
Ti	< 0.5	$SO_4^=$ ⎭	
Zr-Hf	< 0.5	$Co(CN)_6^{==}$	0- 3 mg
V^{IV}, V^V	0-5	$S_4O_6^=$	0-50 mg
Mo^{VI}	< 0.02	pH = 1.3-1.8	

exchange method produces a cake containing over 85 per cent U_3O_8.

The uranium in the above leach liquor is in the hexavalent state U^{VI}. In sulfate solutions, the uranium exists as UO_2^{++} in dynamic equilibrium with its sulfato complexes UO_2SO_4, $UO_2(SO_4)_2^=$, and $UO_2(SO_4)_3^{==}$.

To treat this liquor by cation exchange would involve having a resin which would selectively extract UO_2^{++} in the presence of the much higher concentrations of cations such as Fe^{+++}, Fe^{++}, Al^{+++}, etc. No cation exchanger exhibits selectivity for either uranium cations, U^{++++}, UO_2^{++}, over any of the divalent or trivalent cations.

Fortunately, however, anion-exchange resins do show a selectivity for the uranyl sulfate complexes over that of sulfate and bisulfate ions, and most of the quaternary anion exchangers are able to adsorb uranium from the previously described sulfuric acid leach liquors to almost the complete exclusion of most of the other anions. When the leach liquor is passed through a column of the anion-exchange resin, uranium is adsorbed according to the following equation, where R represents the polymer backbone of the resin.

$$4[R-N(CH_3)_4^+Cl^-] + UO_2(SO_4)_3^{+4-} \rightleftharpoons$$
$$[R-N(CH_3)_4]_4 \, UO_2(SO_4)_3 + 4Cl^-$$

Competing for the ion exchange sites on the resin are also HSO_4^- and $SO_4^=$. Other metals which also form anionic sulfate complexes are Ti, Zr, V, Mo and Th. These metals either form weakly adsorbed complexes or are so low in concentration that they become important only upon repeated cycling.

The ion-exchange adsorption columns used for uranium recovery are no different from any other large commercial deionizing unit. In size, the columns are usually 7 to 8 ft in diameter and contain 200 to 300 cu ft of resin.

The adsorption of uranium takes place by pumping the liquor through a column of anion exchange resin in the chloride (or nitrate form). Leakage throughout the major portion of adsorption is normally less than 0.002 g U_3O_8 per liter.

In water conditioning, the adsorption step is normally stopped at the breakthrough point. In uranium adsorption, regeneration costs are the same whether the resin is fully or only partially saturated. In order to get the maximum use of the resin, the leakage from one column is adsorbed into a second column. In actual practice, a set of three or even four columns is used. As an example of a multicolumn operation consider the following adsorption scheme with three columns A, B and C:

Columns A and B are on adsorption while Column C is on elution. At the point where column B leaks uranium in excess of 0.002 g U_3O_8 per liter, the liquor being fed through A and through B is stopped. At this point the uranium concentration from column A is 80 to 100 per cent of the influent. Column A is then 95 to 100 per cent saturated with uranium. At the point of leakage on column B, one bed volume of fresh water is passed through columns A and B. The pregnant liquor feed is then changed so that column B is the first column on line and column C is the second. We say then that $\overline{BC}$ are on adsorption. While $\overline{BC}$ are on adsorption, column A is being eluted. When C leaks uranium the above changeover is repeated and $\overline{CA}$ are placed on adsorption. This merry-go-round system (Figure 7.1) is repeated constantly. Figure 7.2 depicts a typical resin loading curve.

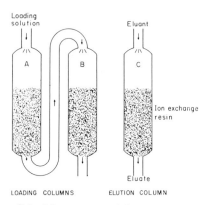

Figure 7.1. Merry-go-round ion-exchange circuit.

The resin in column A, which has been backwashed, is allowed to settle, and is then eluted. The chemistry of the elution is just the reverse of that on adsorption. The equilibrium is driven to the left by using a higher concentration of chloride (or nitrate ion).

In water conditioning one regenerates to a level of maximum utility of the regenerant which will produce a satisfactory water. In uranium recovery, complete regeneration or elution of the uranium is important. Any uranium left on the resin after elution can be lost to the "barren effluent" when the resin column is placed on stream again. For complete removal of uranium 700 per cent of the theoretical nitrate or 2000 per cent of the theoretical amount of chloride must be used. It is obvious that some sort of recycling of the eluting agents must be used.

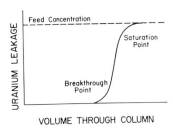

Figure 7.2. Typical uranium loading curve.

The elution of uranium is split into five stages. A typical elution curve is depicted in Figure 7.3. Two holding tanks are required for this system. One contains fresh eluate and one contains recycled eluate (effluent from stage D). A third holding tank containing pregnant eluate is sometimes used, although it may be combined with the precipitation tank.

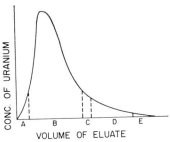

Figure 7.3. Typical elution curve.

Typical eluting solutions used are either mixtures of $HNO_3-NH_4NO_3$ or H_2SO_4-NaCl. The total NO_3^- or Cl^- concentrations are $1.0M$. Flow rates are of the order of 0.1 gal/cu ft/min for nitrate and 0.3 gal/cu ft/min for chloride elutions.

Precipitation

Uranium is recovered from the pregnant eluate (effluent from stages C and D) by precipitation. The pregnant eluate contains not only uranium, but also sulfuric acid which was adsorbed on the resin with uranium, a major portion of the eluting ion (Cl^- or NO_3^-) and a small amount of iron. In some plants, this pregnant eluate (pH $\leqq$ 1) is first treated with lime until the pH raises to about 3.5. This serves to precipitate the iron while 90 per cent or more of the uranium is left in solution. In neutralizing the pregnant eluate, the calcium precipitates sulfate so that an iron cake composed of ferric hydroxide and gypsum is formed. This is filtered, washed with barren eluate, and sent to the leaching section to recover any uranium that coprecipitates with the iron and gypsum.

The filtrate can be treated in any number of ways to precipitate uranium. In qualitative analysis, uranium along with iron is a member of the ammonium hydroxide group. In uranium plants the precipitation of uranium can be effected by adding either NH_3, NaOH or MgO until a pH of 6.8 to 7.0 is reached. The precipitate can be thought of as the diuranate, $Na_2U_2O_7 \cdot xH_2O$ although the amount of cation actually present is less than theoretical. In all probability a considerable amount of $UO_3 \cdot xH_2O$ is also present. The precipitated uranium is then filtered, dried or calcined, and shipped as feed material to one of the uranium refineries. By careful control of all conditions it is possible to obtain a uranium cake approaching 100 per cent U_3O_8 although in actual practice it runs about 85 to 90 per cent for the ammonia-precipitated, calcined cake and a little less when the other agents are used.

The filtrate from the precipitated uranium is adjusted to strength by adding HNO_3 or H_2SO_4-NaCl and it then constitutes the fresh eluate. Since the lime, when used, does not remove all the sulfate present, a certain amount appears in the fresh eluate. In general, the more sulfate present, the less efficient will be the elution. Where a two-stage precipitation is used, the best over-all results are obtained where the sulfate concentration in the fresh eluate is 15 to 20 g $SO_4^=$ per liter.

Recovery of Gold from Cyanide Leach Solutions

A second hydrometallurgical application of ion exchange is the recovery of gold from cyanide leach solutions. This process has been tested on a pilot plant scale and found to be economical. There are still a number of problems to be solved before it becomes sufficiently attractive for any established plant to convert from direct precipitation to ion-exchange concentration.

The current mining practice is to concentrate the gold either by gravity concentration, flotation or even "hand picking" on a large scale. Gold occurs in the ore as the metal. When the ground ore is leached with a dilute (ca. 0.15 per cent KCN) solution the gold is oxidized by air and goes into solution according to the following equation:

$$4Au + 8KCN^* + O_2 + 2H_2O \rightarrow 4KAu(CN)_2 + KOH$$

Other metals leached with the gold include Zn, Ni, Fe, Cu, Ag, Co, etc. These form cyanide complexes such as $Zn(CN)_4^=$, $Ni(CN)_4^=$, $Fe(CN)_6^=$, $Cu(CN)_4^=$, $Ag(CN)_2^-$,

---

* NaCN and $Ca(CN)_2$ are also frequently used.

and $Co(CN)_6^{=}$. The gold concentration in solution is only about 10 ppm present as $Au(CN)_2^-$.

The usual procedure is to filter off the solids and then treat the clear filtrate with zinc dust. The simplest formula for this reaction appears to be:

$$2KAu(CN)_2 + Zn \rightarrow K_2Zn(CN)_4 + 2Au$$

In addition, many side reactions take place with the zinc, so that the precipitated gold may be only 50 per cent pure. This is further refined by smelting to recover pure gold and silver.

In the ion-exchange process, the clear filtrate is passed through a column of a strong base anion exchanger in the chloride form. The cyanide complexes of all the metals are adsorbed along with free cyanide. The adsorbed cyanide complexes are removed by selective elution. Dilute hydrochloric acid removes nickel and zinc. $2M$ sodium cyanide is required to elute iron and copper. The gold is removed by elution with either acetone or methyl alcohol acidified with hydrochloric acid. Strong potassium thiocyanate is required to remove the cobaltous cyanide complex. The gold and silver are recovered from the eluate by distilling off the HCl-organic mixture. Under these reducing conditions metallic gold precipitates.

The advantages of ion exchange over direct precipitation are that in the latter the solutions build up in zinc concentration due to its use as a reductant. It is necessary that a very large portion of the gold barren liquor be recycled. In the ion-exchange recovery step it is possible to recover valuable base metals such as copper, nickel and cobalt.

Recovery of Ions from Sea Water by Ion Exchange

Sea water is a storehouse for many chemical elements. The most abundant metals of any economical significance are magnesium and potassium. Of these, only the first may be recovered efficiently by an ion exchange process although this method of extracting magnesium from sea water has not yet been commercially used. Potassium recovery from sea water has been studied in the laboratory; however, the process does not appear encouraging. In either of these operations, the prime function of the ion exchange operation will be to concentrate the potassium and magnesium.

Recovery of Ions from Waste Streams

Almost every industrial plant has a waste stream of one kind or another. In some cases, these contain valuable metals which can be recovered. In other cases, the ions which appear in waste stream effluents are toxic chemicals which should be treated before disposal. Industrial uses of water are becoming so great that much effort has been placed on cleaning up industrial waste streams to the point where the water is again suitable for process, domestic and agricultural use.

The most important ion-exchange processes in treating waste streams at this time involve chromium plating and anodizing bath wastes, cuprammonium rayon process wastes, and viscose rayon process (zinc sulfate) wastes.

Chrome plating baths consist of a mixture of chromic acid ($H_2Cr_2O_7$) and some sulfuric acid. The non-ion exchange practice is to add CrO_3 periodically to the batch to maintain a concentration of 250 g CrO_3 per liter. Water is also added to make up for evaporation losses as well as liquid loss to the articles being plated. If this last loss (dragout) is not sufficiently high, metal ions build up in the plating bath. These may be nickel or some other metal on which the chrome is being deposited. When this happens a constant bleed must be maintained to remove these ions.

The ion-exchange practice is to dilute the bleed solution

with water to 100 to 120 g CrO_3 per liter. At this level cation-exchange resins of the sulfonated cross-linked polystyrene type will "decationize" the diluted plating solution effectively. The cation exchanger is then regenerated with sulfuric acid. If the cations present are valuable they may be recovered from the spent regenerant by evaporation and crystallization. If they are not valuable, the spent regenerant is either limed and discarded or may be employed for some other operation where impure acid is usable.

The decationized diluted chromic acid solution can be used in part as make-up water for the plating bath. The remainder can be evaporated and used as fresh plating solution. Still a third alternative is its use as an anodizing bath where a concentration of about 100 g CrO_3 per liter is optimum.

Chrome anodizing baths consist of approximately a 10 per cent solution of CrO_3. Using the metal to be anodized as the anode this bath imparts a resistant oxide coating on the metal. Typical of this operation is the anodization of aluminum. In this solution, both Al^{+++} and Cr^{+++} will build up in concentration and reduce the efficiency of the bath.

The treatment here is the same as previously described for the chrome-plating baths. The cation exchanger takes out both the aluminum and the chromic (Cr^{+++}) ions. When regenerated with sulfuric acid the spent regenerant has been found to be an excellent "pickling" solution. Pickling is the process of removing the scale from steels by treatment with a ferric sulfate-sulfuric acid solution.

Every plating operation requires some sort of rinsing operation to remove the excess electrolyte from the surface of materials being plated. In the chrome-plating field, this rinse water is of the order of 100 to 500 ppm $CrO_4^=$. Since the chromium to be recovered is to be adsorbed by the resin, anion-exchange resins are used. Quaternary ammonium strong base anion-exchange resins are employed in this operation. Since these anion exchangers are less resistant to oxidation than are the cation exchangers, the oxidizing ability of the acid solution is reduced by first neutralizing with sodium hydroxide. The resultant Na_2CrO_4 is then passed through the anion exchanger, giving an effluent consisting of sodium hydroxide. The resin is regenerated with 10 to 15 per cent NaOH to give a $NaOH-Na_2CrO_4$ mixture which is passed through a sulfonic acid cation exchange resin to convert the sodium chromate to pure chromic acid.

In the manufacture of Bemberg rayon and cotton staple fiber ion exchange is used to recover copper economically. The fiber process itself utilizes the solubility of cellulose in an ammoniacal copper solution and the resulting blue, viscous cellulose liquor is then extruded into softened water to coagulate the plastic filaments. The cuprammonium filaments are further treated with sulfuric acid to destroy the cuprammonium complex and precipitate the cellulose.

The softened water treatment gives a waste solution (blue water) containing about a 0.1 g Cu per liter and 1 g NH_3 per liter at pH = 10. The acid treatment gives a waste liquor containing about 20 g Cu per liter and 65 g H_2SO_4 per liter. In the ion-exchange recovery process, copper is recovered commercially from the blue water by using a cation-exchange resin of the carboxylic acid in the acid form,

$$Cu(NH_3)_4^{++} + 2H^+R^- \rightarrow Cu(NH_3)_2R_2 + 2NH_4^+.$$

The resin is regenerated using the acid waste water already containing about 20 g Cu per liter. The regenerant is further treated with ammonia to a pH 4.3. At this pH the copper remains in solution but degraded cellulose, pigments, silica, etc. are precipitated and filtered. The pH is then raised to 7 where the copper precipitates as a basic copper sulfate, $Cu(OH)_2 \cdot CuSO_4$. The copper is then in a state in which it can be treated with ammonia and reused to dissolve more cellulose. The effluent from the ion-exchange recovery of copper from the blue water contains free ammonia, which can be recovered by vacuum distillation. The water itself is of sufficiently good quality to be reused.

The viscose process for manufacturing rayon involves reacting the sodium salt of cellulose with carbon disulfide (CS_2) to form a cellulose xanthate. This solution is then extruded as fiber filaments into a solution containing sulfuric acid and zinc sulfate (hardening agent) to regenerate the cellulose.

When the fiber is rinsed, a waste solution of sulfuric acid and zinc sulfate is obtained. This solution (100 ppm Zn) is treated with a sulfonic acid cation exchanger to recover the zinc. The original sulfuric acid-zinc sulfate solution can be used as a regenerant, since the sulfuric acid concentration is sufficiently high that little of the contained zinc is adsorbed by the resin.

This process not only provides an answer to a waste problem but also recovers sufficient zinc to pay for its operation.

Separation of Chemically Similar Elements

When one considers the column ion-exchange process as one of continuously adsorbing and desorbing ions, it is apparent that some degree of separation must be taking place since no two ions have exactly the same affinity for the ion-exchange sites of the exchanger. In some operations one foot of resin can be considered equivalent to 100 or more stages of separation, such as fractional distillation or fractional precipitation.

The real test of ion exchange in this respect is the separation of rare earths, whose atomic numbers range from 58 to 71. Chemically, yttrium, atomic number 39, and lanthanum, atomic number 57, are so similar to the rare earths that these are also included. The rare earths are so much alike chemically that any means of separation such as precipitation separate only groups of rare earths, never individual elements. By repeated crystallization (several thousand times) it has been possible to recover some of the rare earths with a purity of 98 to 99 per cent.

In the very early ion-exchange work on rare earths, a solution of these elements was passed over a column of a sulfonic cation exchanger and, although some enrichment of individual rare earths was achieved during this operation, it was apparent that an extremely long separation zone would be required. To enhance this separation, a chromatographic technique has been developed which employs a solution of citric acid adjusted to a pH 5 to 8 with ammonia, which is passed over the column to move the rare earths previously adsorbed at the top of the resin column. The purpose of the citric acid is to superimpose the slightly different affinity of the rare earths toward citric acid upon the still less different affinity of the rare earths for the resin. This technique was discussed in Chapter 5.

For any particular series of ions, the smaller the ion, the more stable is its ionic complex. Lutetium, atomic number 71, is smaller than ytterbium, atomic number 70, which in term is smaller than thulium, atomic number 69, and so on. Thus, when the citric acid is passed through the resin, element 71 moves faster down the column than all the others, since it has the greatest tendency to form a non-adsorbed soluble complex with the citric acid. When elutions are carried out in this manner, the rare earths appear in the effluent in a series of characteristic bell-shaped elution curves (Figure 7.4). These elution curves may, however, overlap slightly. Individual rare earths obtained by these methods are in excess of 99.9 per cent purity.

An improvement with respect to economy of operation

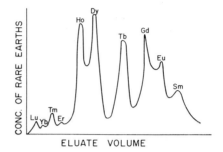

Figure 7.4. Fractionation of rare earths by
ion-exchange chromatography.

has been developed involving the substitution of ethylene-
diamine tetracetic acid (EDTA) for citric acid. The complex
constants for EDTA with the rare earths are larger than for
citric acid. Since the free acid of EDTA is insoluble, cupric
ion (Cu^{++}) is used for saturating the resin prior to loading
the column with the rare earth mixture. This last system is
currently being used on a plant scale.

Other Separations of Chemically Similar Elements

Noteworthy of mention are the ion exchange separations
of such pairs of elements as zirconium-hafnium, niobium
(columbium)-tantalum, cobalt-nickel, and the platinum
metals. Given any two elements which can form ions in
solution, it is possible to effect their separations by choosing
the proper solution conditions and the proper resin.

8. MISCELLANEOUS APPLICATIONS*

In this chapter, an attempt will be made to describe and discuss selected applications of ion exchange in order that those who are new to the field may note the widespread utility that this phenomenon is enjoying. Although many of these applications may appear to be of academic interest only, it is important to realize that commercial ion-exchange applications have developed from investigations that were originally academic.

ANALYTICAL CHEMISTRY

Ion-exchange techniques have become a routine matter in many phases of analytical chemistry. Many of the every-day routine analyses performed in industrial and academic laboratories are tedious and time-consuming because of crystallizations, fractional precipitations, distillations and other upgrading or purifying steps designed to eliminate interfering compounds or ions and to concentrate the constituent to be analyzed. In other cases, cations or anions that are very similar in chemical properties can be analyzed only after repeated separation procedures. The ultimate analyses are subject to large errors as a result of cumulative errors in each step. Frequently, an analyst must determine a constituent that is present in only trace amounts and can

* This chapter was written in cooperation with Mr. Charles Dickert of the Rohm & Haas Co.

become involved in costly equipment or spend considerable time in devising an elaborate test procedure. All these problems have been considered from an ion-exchange point of view and a few of many such applications are listed below to illustrate each of the above cases.

Removal of Interfering Ions

Calcium and barium analyses by the oxalate or sulfate method are frequently in error as a result of phosphate ions present in the solution which coprecipitate with the calcium and barium. Since the phosphate has a negative charge which is opposite to the positive charge of calcium and barium, passage of a solution of the mixture through a sulfonic acid cation exchanger results in the adsorption of the calcium and barium allowing the phosphate ions to remain unadsorbed in the solution. Analysis by precipitation is completed after removing or eluting the cations (calcium and barium) from the ion-exchange resin with an ammonium chloride solution.

Another application that is somewhat similar is the detection and identification of the transuranic elements (elements 93-102) resulting from nuclear reactions. Other elements that are also present in solution and interfere with analysis are eliminated by selective adsorption and elution of the desired element on a strong-base ion-exchange resin. An anion exchange resin is used since the transuranic metals form anionic complexes in acidic solutions.

Separation of Similar and Closely Related Ions

One of the best examples is the analysis of rare earths; it involves a chromatographic or a cation-exchanger separation with a chelating agent as the eluant. A more detailed description of this technique is given in Chapter 7.

Anion-exchange resins have been used in a similar manner for the separation of chloride, bromide and iodide ions. Many separations have been reported by medical, food and biochemical research laboratories for complex organic compounds of similar structure. The applications are useful to the extent that complete separations and quantitative analyses are greatly facilitated.

The alkaloids atropine, strychnine, morphine, etc., have been effectively separated by selective adsorption and elution from anion-exchange resins. Morphine has been separated from codeine by strong-base ion-exchange resins, the separation depending on the hydroxyl group (phenolic) present in the morphine structure. Codeine lacks the phenolic group and is therefore unadsorbed.

A separation of the nucleotides of ribonucleic acid, an important compound in cell structure, is possible by adsorption of the nucleotides on a strong-base resin and separation by selective elution. The strong-base resins have also been used for separation of neutral from weak and strong amino acids. Further separation is possible by employing a weak-base resin to extract the strong amino acids (dicarboxylics) and allowing the weak amino acids (monocarboxylics) to pass through the resin unadsorbed. All the amino acids can be separated by ion-exchange chromatography on a sulfonic acid cation exchange resin (Figure 8.1).

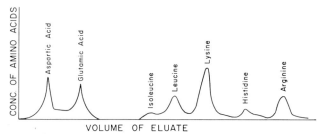

Figure 8.1. Ion-exchange chromatography of amino acids.

Strong-base resins have aided in separating antihistiminic and other similar compounds. The cation exchangers can also be used for such applications. Considerable interest exists in determining the flavonoids present in various plants. The juice of fresh-cut plants or fruit is passed through a strong acid ion exchanger and the flavonoids are extracted from the juice.

Trace Analysis

Frequently it is desired to analyze for constituents present in solution in trace amounts. Analyses can be made by using special and expensive equipment or by time-consuming development of analytical procedures. These procedures have been greatly simplified by use of ion-exchange resins. As an example, the copper content of milk can be determined by passing milk through a strong acid cation exchanger. Copper is adsorbed and after a suitable volume of milk has passed through, the copper is removed from the resin and the resulting effluent analyzed for copper. Having determined the amount of copper and knowing the volume of milk treated, the concentration of copper in the milk is readily calculated.

Copper occurring in mineral oils as copper naphthenate in a concentration range of 1 to 57 ppm has been successfully determined by passing mineral oil through a cation-exchange resin, which adsorbs copper.

Determination of Concentration

A solution containing HCl, NaCl and $NaNO_3$, for example, can be analyzed for H^+ and Cl^- by simple titrations. Nitrate determinations usually are more complex. If, however, a known quantity of the solution is passed through a strong-acid ion exchanger in the hydrogen form, the sodium ions replace hydrogen to form HCl and HNO_3 in the effluent. The difference between hydrogen-ion concentration of the effluent and the chloride concentration of the influent is equivalent to the nitrate concentration of the influent. Many other determinations involving sulfate and phosphate ions in addition to or in place of chloride and nitrate ions indicated above are possible with ion-exchange resins.

These are but a few of the many industrial and research applications where ion-exchange resins can serve as time- and money-saving tools. Exchange resins are now widely recognized as an analytical tool and in certain cases are as important to analytical chemists as are burettes containing standardized acid and base solutions.

Ion-exchange resins are commonly used in the spherical or granular form. Since ion exchange rates are diffusion controlled, when ground to a very small size (200 mesh or smaller), the resin exhibits an over-all higher ion exchange rate since many of the internal sites of a bead have become external as a result of fine grinding. The larger surface area of small particles allows easier separation of two ions which are both adsorbed, but with different selectivity. Although two or more ions may initially be adsorbed at the top of the resin bed, the ion which is more easily adsorbed will displace the other ion from the exchange sites as additional solution is passed through. The ions removed will in turn be adsorbed further down the bed until finally zones exist in the resin column which consist almost entirely of a particular ion in a particular zone. Such separations are termed chromatographic, and the resins are designated as chromatographic grade. Separations using larger particle size resins are not as efficient or complete, since the actual separation is slowed down by diffusion of ions in and out of the resin matrix. Flow rate is a most important factor when using large particle resins. Chromatographic grade resins are easy to use on a small scale for analytical purposes, but they become a problem on a large scale because of the small particle size and the resulting high pressure drop across the resin bed.

Many chemical identifications have been made by the use of special paper (although ordinary filter paper will work in many cases) to separate one component from another. Recently, fine particle size resin has been incorporated into paper to effect chromatographic separations similar to columnar separations which will aid in identifying chemicals.

PHARMACOLOGICAL AND MEDICAL APPLICATIONS

Several illustrations mentioned in the preceding section touched on analyses of a biochemical nature. These uses have been recognized by pharmaceutical houses and the medical profession and have advanced from analytical procedures to the direct application of purifying many organic compounds occurring in nature or prepared synthetically. Ion-exchange resins have been used as analytical reagents acting in the human body, as carriers for drugs, as aids or substitutes for carrying out bodily functions, and for control of disorders on the external tissues of the body. The applications are too numerous to discuss in detail, but the following illustrations will give an idea of the broadness of use in this field.

Several reports have been issued on the purification of viruses by use of strong-base anion exchangers. Purification is effected by passing a tissue suspension through the resin bed, the resin adsorbing most of the nitrogenous material (65 to 99 per cent). Viruses of encephalitis, rabies and the Lansing strain of poliomyelitis have been purified in this manner.

Some antibiotics can be purified by adsorption of the antibiotic with a cation exchanger, leaving unwanted constituents in the mother liquor. The antibiotic is eluted from the resin with a strong acid and subsequently precipitated from the aqueous solution. The carboxylic cation exchanger is used for extracting, concentrating, and purifying all the streptomycin and neomycin now produced. Recovery and purification of Vitamin B_{12} can be accomplished with the same resin.

Ion-exchange resins serve as very interesting tools for carrying out analytical procedures within the body. As an example, the HCl content of gastric juice is determined by feeding the patient a portion of the quinine or cationic dye salt of a carboxylic cation exchanger. As the resin contacts the gastric juice in the stomach, the HCl present in the juice releases quinine or dye from the resin in proportion to the stomach acidity. The released quinine or dye is eliminated from the body in the urine and the color or fluorescence of the urine is measured visually.

Ulcers, associated with excess HCl in the stomach, are treated with a finely divided weak-base resin. Such treatment has proved quite satisfactory in giving relief to those suffering from such ulcers.

Cardiac edema is characterized by abnormal body swelling and high blood pressure caused by a high sodium content in the body brought about by the inability of the kidney to excrete sufficient sodium. Oral administration of weak acid resins of high capacity, such as "Amberlite" IRC-50, has been successful in supplementing the function of the kidney in removing sodium.

A finely ground version of a weak-base resin in combination with kaolin has been successfully administered for control of diarrhea. The function of the resin is to adsorb acidic poisons causing the disorder. Here again resins may be considered as aiding a particular organ in carrying out its function, particularly when an irregularity is present. Blood has also been treated with ion-exchange resins for various purposes, including isolation of important fractions and improvement of storage quality.

Some vital drugs are difficult to administer orally because of objection to their taste. Recent studies have shown these difficulties may be eliminated by first adsorbing the drug on an ion-exchange resin and feeding the drug in this manner. The drug, para-aminosalicylic acid, is administered in this way in the treatment of tuberculosis.

Resins can even be used for certain skin disorders. Typical uses are antiperspirants, poison ivy salves and applications for athlete's foot. The latter application involves the cobalt form of a carboxylic cation-exchange resin.

Ion-exchange resins can be used for removal of unwanted substances in foods and thus become important steps in processing food. Wines and juices, when left standing for an extended time, develop cloudiness and sediment on the bottom of the bottle even though sealed. The precipitation of potassium acid tartrate (potassium bitartrate) can be avoided by passing the wine or juice through a cation-exchange resin in the sodium form to give the more soluble sodium compound, the potassium being retained by the resin. The only other way sedimentation on standing can be prevented is to store the wine or juice at a reduced temperature for long periods of time and then to filter before bottling. The low temperature causes precipitation due to the lower solubility of potassium bitartrate, but the cost of refrigeration is considerable.

Considerable research has been undertaken on milk and milk products with the aim of improving properties of the stored form and of modifying certain characteristics of milk so that they can be better utilized for certain uses. Ordinary milk contains some calcium and might therefore be termed "hard" milk. When this milk reaches the digestive tract it forms hard curds which are somewhat difficult to digest, especially in infants. This is the primary reason why babies not nursed with mother's milk are formula-fed rather than fed with ordinary milk. A baby's digestive system is not sufficiently mature to digest the hard curd. The soft and easily digested curd of mother's milk is a result of low calcium content. Consequently, cation-exchange resins in the sodium form are used as a means of "softening" ordinary cow's milk.

Considerable progress has been made during recent years in purifying sugar with ion-exchange resins. Sugar, when extracted from beets or cane, contains inorganic solids (ash), organic compounds which give sugar an off-color, amino acids, etc. which limit the economical recovery of all the sugar present. Because of these impurities a considerable amount of sugar remains as molasses. It has been demonstrated that ion-exchange resins can be employed in beet and cane refining resulting in higher quality sugars and economic savings.

The type of ion-exchange resin employed depends on the source of the sugar to be refined. Raw cane sugar, imported from countries such as Cuba, contains crystals of 97 per cent sucrose and about 0.5 per cent ash and 0.5 per cent non-sugar organic compounds. The sugar is melted (dissolved in hot recycle sugar sirup) prior to purification. The normal purification steps involve flocculation of colloids followed by carbon or bonechar treatment and subsequent crystallization of white sugar. Due to molasses formation, all the sugar in the solution cannot be recovered. Ion exchange has been employed successfully in various sugar refineries for increasing sugar yields and quality. Various ion-exchange processes have been developed which serve to reduce the impurities (ash, color, amino acids, etc.) that prevent complete crystallization of sucrose.

The cation-exchange resin normally employed for cane sugar refining is a weak acid of the carboxylic acid type. Studies have shown that high amounts of invert sugar are formed in concentrated sugar solutions if passed through a strong acid exchanger at elevated temperatures. The carboxylic resin is employed in a Monobed with a porous quaternary anion exchange resin. Sugar sirups treated by such a system have unusually high purities. The organic impurities of the sugar that contribute color are weak organic acids that can be removed by utilizing the porous strong-base resin in the chloride form. A porous resin is necessary to allow rapid diffusion of large organic molecules into the resin beads.

Other types of resins are used for refining beet sugar, since the sugar is refined immediately after extraction from the sliced sugar beets. The use of a low temperature permits the use of the strong-acid cation exchanger without high production of invert sugar. The acid juice resulting from contacting the cation exchanger is then passed through an anion exchange for deionization and decolorization. The organic acids extracted from the beets are stronger than those present in cane sugar, and thus permit the use of weak-base anion-exchange resins for removal of the acidic color bodies.

Ion-exchange techniques are gradually being adopted by various sugar refineries throughout the world.

CHEMICAL PROCESSING

There are many miscellaneous uses of ion-exchange resins that cannot be described in detail in this chapter, but should be mentioned.

Lactose can be recovered from milk as a relatively pure product by passing milk through a cation-exchange resin in the hydrogen form and heating the effluent to coagulate the remaining nitrogenous compounds.

Glycerin is purified of ionized solids, color, and odor-producing compounds by passing the glycerin solution through a cation-anion series column or a Monobed unit. The resins used should be strong-acid and strong-base exchangers which are capable of splitting and adsorbing the ionic solids; they should be in the hydrogen and hydroxyl forms so that water is the product of exchange.

Because of the corrosive action of HCl, concentrated HCl usually contains a sufficient amount of iron to give it a yellow color. Iron (ferric, Fe^{+++}) is complexed in concentrated HCl as an anion of the $FeCl_6^{---}$ type. When the acid is passed through a strong-base anion-exchange resin in the chloride form, the anionic complex of iron is readily retained by the ion-exchange bed. The acid solution coming from the bottom of the column is water-white and free of iron. It is collected until iron begins to leak through. At this point, the resin is almost saturated with iron, and regeneration is required. The regenerant is simple and cheap—water. By passing water through the resin bed, the ferric chloride complex is broken down into a cation species and therefore cannot be retained by an anion exchanger; thus iron is removed or eluted from the resin. The resin remains in the chloride form and is ready for the next cycle. It is important to note that the iron must be in the oxidized state (Fe^{+++}) since reduced iron (Fe^{++}) does not form anionic complexes.

Resins are reported to have been used for the preparation of hydrogen peroxide, H_2O_2, from Na_2O_2. This preparation would involve passing a Na_2O_2 solution through a cation exchange resin in the hydrogen form. Metals can be removed from H_2O_2 by the same resin. It is reported that 35 per cent H_2O_2 has been so purified. Resin stability is poor under these conditions.

Petroleum contains odoriferous compounds called mercaptans. These compounds resemble alcohol but have an atom of sulfur in place of oxygen. They may be designated as RSH where R is a carbon chain. The mercaptans can be removed by passing petroleum through a strong-base resin in the hydroxyl form. Mercaptans in other solutions can be removed in a similar manner.

As the population density of the country increases, state laws are becoming more rigid with respect to stream pollution. Consequently, many industries are being faced with a problem of cleaning up waste effluents before they leave the plant. Many companies involved in metal-plating operations have found it imperative to remove metals such as chromium, nickel, copper, zinc, etc. Such problems are usually solved satisfactorily by ion-exchange techniques, although some care must be exercised in selecting the most efficient and/or most economic resin. Frequently, certain anions such as cyanide are also present in the waste streams and must also be removed. Phenols have long been a problem of effluent streams from petroleum and coke-oven by-product plants. Investigations have shown that strong-base resins effectively remove phenolic compounds from these streams. The use of ion-exchange resins as a control for stream pollution is expected to increase as laws become more widespread and more rigid. One important consideration in using resins for this purpose is that some materials previously dumped can now be recovered economically and reused.

Some industries require ultra-pure water in processing and have turned to ion exchange for this purpose. This is particularly true in photographic laboratories and television tube assembly lines where trace quantities of certain anions or metallic cations can seriously affect quality of the finished product.

CATALYSIS

Catalysts are agents employed in a chemical reaction to increase the speed or rate at which the reaction takes place. The catalyst enters into the reaction only to the extent that it aids in forming an excited or activated state in one phase of the reaction which is usually impossible to attain by simply mixing the reactants necessary to produce the desired product. In the course of the reaction, the catalyst is neither consumed nor destroyed. Reactions may be catalyzed by either acid or base, and normally aqueous solutions are used. While the catalyst is not destroyed during a reaction, it frequently must be destroyed by neutralization after the reaction is completed, in order to recover the product.

Since ion-exchange materials are considered as insoluble acids and bases, a logical step is to use ion-exchange resins as a catalyst rather than the customary soluble acids and bases. Cation exchangers have been employed successfully for catalyzing the reactions involved in preparing invert sugar sirups, cracking of petroleum to form gasoline, and preparing esters used as perfume intermediates.

The advantages of ion-exchange catalysis are: (1) ease of recovery (filtration, etc.); (2) neutralization not required; (3) product not diluted; (4) corrosion problems reduced; (5) starting material and product sensitivity to pH practically eliminated; and (6) production of side products reduced. The only major disadvantage is a temperature limitation which more or less restricts the use of resins as catalysts to reactions occurring at temperatures below 100°C.* Above this temperature, the resin degrades or loses active sites and becomes useless as a catalyst. The alumino-silicates, however, can be used at much higher temperatures.

The miscellaneous applications of ion-exchange resins have been confined to date to substances which are solids in either spherical or granular form. Other forms exist which can be classified as films and fibers. An ion exchanger need not be a solid; it can exist as a liquid. But in order to be

---

* This temperature limitation is for the acid form of sulfonic acid cation exchangers. The basic forms of anion exchangers are limited to temperatures below 60°C.

useful as a liquid exchanger two principal properties must be present: (1) water insolubility and (2) capacity to exchange ions. Fibers, membranes and liquid exchangers have not been discussed in detail since the same principles governing exchange when using ion-exchange resins also prevail for these substances. The deviation in form only allows more freedom in process design. The liquid exchangers, high molecular weight organic amines and phosphoric acid derivatives, are being employed commercially for recovering and purifying uranium. Membranes are now being employed on a large scale in electrodialysis multiple membrane cells for desalting brackish waters in the United States, South Africa, and North Africa.

9. ION-EXCHANGE ENGINEERING*

Engineering implies the design of equipment, of process arrangement, and of structure for a given purpose. In a broad sense, engineering is also responsible for "fitting" a process into a large operation, for the changes to be incurred by such processes, and for the economics of operation. The ion-exchange engineer plays an important part in these problems. He is required to predict the physical and chemical performance of an ion-exchange material under standard conditions. He is also expected to design the details of the equipment and to have opinions on the suitability of certain types of designs.

PHYSICAL PROPERTIES OF ION-EXCHANGE MATERIAL AS RELATED TO ENGINEERING PRACTICE

In an engineering design, the physical properties of the exchanger play essential roles. Before a column of an ion-exchange material can operate properly, the solution must be able to flow through the bed uniformly and with a minimum of difficulty. Particle size is extremely important, since it determines the resistance to flow to be expected. This resistance gives rise to pressure drop and controls the degree of expansion during the backwash. Other factors affecting these hydraulic properties are temperature, particle density and particle shape.

---

* This chapter was written in cooperation with Mr. F. X. McGarvey of the Rohm & Haas Co.

Hydraulics

The resistance to flow through a bed or column of an ion exchanger has a most important bearing on the design of an ion-exchange plant. The most important hydraulic properties of an ion-exchange column are the pressure drop across the column during operation and the expansion of the bed during the backwash operation. Indeed the effect of the hydraulics of ion-exchange material on the design of an ion-exchange plant can hardly be overemphasized. Most difficulties in operation are due to a lack of consideration of hydraulics during the design stage. The pressure drop resulting from the flow of solution through ion-exchange equipment is due to the ion exchanger as well as to the valves and piping. The engineer designing an ion-exchange plant must know the hydraulics of ion-exchange materials in order to specify proper piping and sufficient pumping capacity, and to be sure that the treated solution will be at the desired pressure, and that sufficient space be available in the unit for proper backwashing of resin for colloid and sediment removal at all possible ambient temperatures.

The hydraulic pressure drop data available for ion exchangers are best correlated by plotting either psi/ft of bed depth *vs* flow rate in gal/min/sq ft of cross-sectional exchanger bed area or ft of H_2O/ft of bed *vs* gpm/sq ft. The relationships, 1 atm = 14.7 psi = 33.9 ft H_2O = 29.92 in Hg, will enable one to calculate data for most systems. Flow is expressed as a velocity term in hydraulics and differs from the contact time measure used for exchange rate (gpm/cu ft). Pressure drop is a function of a variety of factors such as particle size, particle shape, viscosity, temperature, etc. The pressure drop will increase as the particle size of the exchanger and the volume between the particles (voids) decrease. An increase of the viscosity of the liquid will also increase the pressure drop. For a given exchanger, solution conditions and column dimensions, the pressure drop will increase with increasing flow rate.

Bed expansion results from backwashing. Backwashing is required to cleanse the bed of foreign materials. If these foreign materials are allowed to remain in the bed, the bed will pack and channels will appear resulting in poor flow distribution. Designers of ion-exchange equipment should provide sufficient room for expansion so that the bed may be washed completely but without loss of exchanger through the top distributor. It is the job of the engineer to estimate the amount of expansion which will result when an exchanger is backwashed.

In many respects, head loss (pressure drop) and bed expansion are related, since resistance to flow determines the lifting power of the liquid. In addition, screen size distribution (uniformity coefficient), true particle density, and liquid density play important roles. Efforts to correlate these various factors into a single relationship have not been entirely successful.

The hydraulics of backwashing a bed of an exchanger are dependent upon particle size, particle shape, particle density, solution density, solution viscosity, temperature, etc. As one increases the particle size, density, void volume, and temperature, one can backwash at a higher flow rate without increasing bed expansion excessively and therefore obtain a better cleansing of the bed and classification.

UNIT DESIGN

Once the resin volume has been calculated from experimental data for a particular job, the unit must be designed from a mechanical standpoint. The first problem is to "size" the tank to hold the resin and the various components required to distribute the liquid. This problem of distribution is very important and provision must be made to distribute liquid for purposes of backwashing, regeneration, and exhaustion. Since these flows differ widely, the distribution design must be flexible enough to accommodate all conditions.

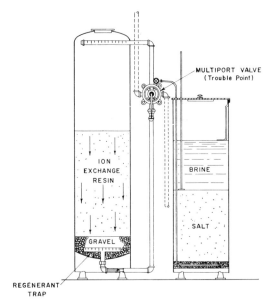

Figure 9.1. Domestic softener.

Distribution is accomplished by a network of pipes frequently originating from a common hub. The pipes have small holes or valves in them which are located at even spacing from the standpoint of tank cross-sectional areas. The holes and pipes are of diameter such that the distributor will be under pressure at the lowest flows and will still not have too high a resistance at the highest flow. If the difference in flows is too great, two distributors may be required. The holes may be spaced according to diameter (usually ¼ to ¹⁄₁₆ in. in diameter) so that the small holes are near the center and become larger as they reach the end. While the hub distributor is quite common, many engineering companies build much simpler ones, consisting of baffle plates or just inlet pipes pointed to the top of the tank.

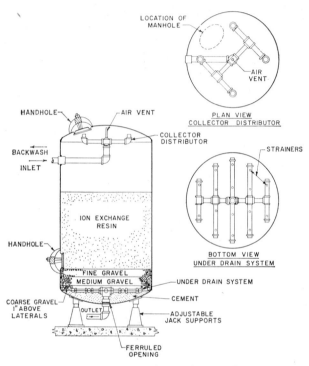

Figure 9.2. Industrial ion-exchange softener.

Since the holes in the distributor are larger than the exchanger particles, the lower one must be placed in a support bed of graded gravel or be covered by screens. Normally, the support bed consists of graded coal or gravel. This is placed carefully in layers with the largest size on the bottom. The particle size ranges from ½ to ¼ in. in the lowest layer

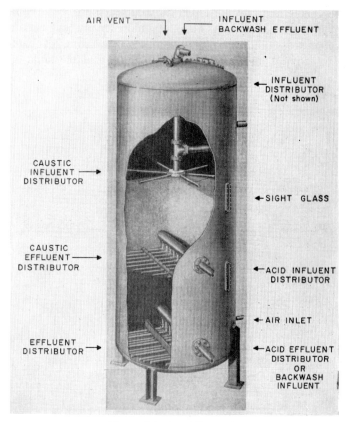

Figure 9.3. Monobed unit.

of about 2 to 3 in. depth. Placed midway is a ¼ to ⅛ in. layer to a depth of 2 to 3 in., and finally a layer of ⅛ to ¹⁄₅₀ in. material is placed on top. All components should be carefully washed before use.

The exchanger is placed in the unit above the graded gravel. Normally the shell should be partially filled with water and the resin dumped into the unit through the water. This is not entirely necessary, and for a large unit may be a disadvantage. When the proper weight of resin has been added, the bed should be carefully backwashed to remove dirt, fines and air. The position of the top of the bed should be located with reference to some structural point so that the resin inventory can be checked.

(Courtesy Graver Water Conditioning Co.)

Figure 9.4. A medium size commercial ion-exchange installation.

The height of bed may be varied between 2 and 10 ft, most installations averaging 4 to 5 ft. Sufficient side wall must be provided to permit 50 per cent bed expansion for cation exchangers. The lighter anion exchangers require allowance for 100 per cent expansion. Excessively deep beds result in high pressure drops with a resulting danger in channelling. Channels resulting from contamination may be serious enough to force exchanger particles through the underdrain.

Figures 9.1 to 9.6 illustrate the basic elements of several commercial ion-exchange units.

(Courtesy Graver Water Conditioning Co.)

Figure 9.5. A large commercial ion-exchange installation.

The design of an ion exchange installation depends upon ratings on exchangers under specific conditions. In water conditioning, the manufacturers of ion-exchange materials have developed a considerable amount of data for their products which will permit an engineer to design a plant for treating various water supplies. It is essential, however, that an accurate analysis of the solution to be treated, the maximum flow rate, and the specifications on the treated water be available.

The major cost of most ion-exchange operations is the summation of chemical consumption, depreciation on equipment, space rental, taxes, labor, etc. Labor is a more important factor than depreciation and approaches chemical cost in value. This is particularly true for the small plants. Normally, for large installations, one may assume that one or two men per shift will be able to handle any well designed plant. This may be a full time job or may only represent a partial activity. A chemist may also be required for control work. Equipment will normally be rated at a 10-20 year life

(Courtesy Dorr-Oliver Co.)

Figure 9.6. Control panel for large commercial ion-exchange installation.

and may be charged off with interest under such a program. Resin life may be handled separately; it can represent an appreciable amount if the life is not well known. An accurate estimate of resin life is very important to such calculations.

In general, the combined cost of all these factors rarely approaches the expenditure due to chemical consumption; but for every installation there is an optimum cycle length and equipment size. The problem of selection becomes one of trial-and-error calculation of the variables for a particular installation. Recently, electronic computers have been employed to eliminate the trial-and-error method and make design and operation calculations more accurate.

SPECIAL ENGINEERING

The use of ion-exchange resins in special ways or in conventional applications by special continuous procedures requires some discussion. The first method which comes to mind is a continuous countercurrent operation employing ion-exchange particles in a fluidized state. This is accomplished by eduction of the exchanger from one contactor to another. The location of these streams and of the eduction fluids can be arranged so the exchanger is dumped into the various contactors. Since the resin cannot be pumped effectively and safely, the design of eductors becomes very important. Efforts to scale-up this design have not been too encouraging, although continuous processes are being developed.

In 1955, a continuous countercurrent process was devised to handle pulp slurries in the mining industry. This consists of a series of baskets which contain the resin. The slurry to be treated passes down under gravity potential through the baskets. The baskets are agitated to keep the resin in contact with the slurry. This is accomplished by a series of baskets moving up and down in the pulp slurry.

While many interesting special methods are under study, very few large-scale installations have been constructed which deviate from the standard columnar concurrent technique.

10. THE FUTURE OF ION EXCHANGE

The future of any development may be considered by means of many criteria. Since ion exchange is both an important phase of many natural phenomena and since it may be used as an important tool, technologists and scientists will continue to be interested in ion exchange for many years to come.

What developments and discoveries are on the horizon? From a theoretical viewpoint, a more quantitative understanding of the equilibria and kinetics of ion exchange must be realized. Our present understanding does not permit one to predict accurately the course of ion-exchange reactions and to design equipment for ion-exchange processes with a minimum of experimentation. The theoretical studies necessary are quite difficult and involved and probably will necessitate prior studies on simple, non-crosslinked polymer systems.

New technological developments will also depend upon the commercial availability of improved and new ion-exchange materials, both organic and inorganic. Exchangers that can be employed for long periods of time at temperatures above 100°C are being sought. Exchangers whose life stability are an order of magnitude greater than present materials will extend the industrial usefulness of ion exchange. Although the inorganic exchangers were studied for many years before the advent of the resinous exchangers, their study has been sorely neglected during the past two decades. The need for thermally stable ion exchangers has begun to stimulate activity in this direction.

Ion exchangers of high specificity have intrigued many investigators. Although the commercial development of such materials has not come to pass, notable strides have been made. A resin highly specific for copper and another for boric acid have been prepared and studied.

Considerable progress is being made in preparing exchangers of varying physical structures designed to take advantage of engineering advances. Liquid ion exchange, a development in its infancy, promises to extend the scope of ion exchange. Ion-exchange filter papers and fibers have been prepared and studied. The development of ion-exchange permselective membranes has opened up new possibilities in the realm of electrochemistry. These membranes are now being used in South Africa, North Africa, the United States, and the Near East for preparing potable water from brackish waters. Improvements in membranes will undoubtedly broaden the utility of these unusual materials. An order of magnitude improvement in their electrochemical properties would make them extremely useful for preparing potable water from sea water.

From an application viewpoint, there exists no dearth of ideas. As more is learned of the basic phenomena associated with ion exchange, more useful techniques and applications are revealed. For example, it has only been in recent years that many useful applications could be accomplished with ion exchange materials in which no exchange of ions is involved. These depend upon the fact that many ion-exchange materials, particularly the resins, behave as highly concentrated aqueous solutions of polyelectrolytes that are totally immiscible in other solutions. It is this property that permits one to prepare permselective ion-exchange membranes, the heart of the electrolytic membrane cell employed for preparing potable water from brackish water. The same property enables one to employ these materials as acidic and basic catalysts. Non-ion exchange separations are also possible with these materials. These include the separation of mixtures of ionic and non-ionic species (ion exclusion) and the separation of nonelectrolytes (salting-in chromatography).

The first century of ion exchange has witnessed a remarkable series of developments rivaled by few other phenomena.

APPENDIX 1

ION-EXCHANGE CALCULATIONS

One of the major calculations made in ion-exchange technology involves the determination of the quantity of ion exchanger necessary to treat a given amount of liquid in a given period. In order to solve such problems, it is necessary to have at least the following basic data beforehand:

(1) an analysis of the solution to be treated
(2) the volume of solution to be treated per unit time
(3) desired frequency of regeneration
(4) performance limitations of exchanger being considered

For the major areas of application, the manufacturer of the standard ion-exchange materials publishes sufficient performance data for his products that enable the designer of equipment to conduct the necessary design calculations with a fair degree of accuracy without any experimentation. The following problems are typical of most ion exchange calculations:

Problem:

A water of the composition described in Table A.1 is to be softened to less than five parts per million hardness by means of a high capacity sulfonic acid cation exchange resin. The unit must treat 20,000 gallons per day with a frequency of regeneration of once per day. Sufficient storage facilities are available to handle the water demand during the regeneration period. What quantity of resin is needed for this job?

TABLE A.1. ANALYSIS OF UNTREATED WATER SUPPLY

Constituent	(ppm as CaCo₃)*
Calcium (Ca)	150
Magnesium (Mg)	50
Potassium (K)	5
Sodium (Na)	5
Total hardness	200

* In water analysis, it is convenient to calculate all constituents on a calcium carbonate ($CaCO_3$) equivalent basis.

TABLE A.2. OPERATIONAL CHARACTERISTICS OF HIGH CAPACITY SULFONIC ACID CATION EXCHANGE RESIN

Regeneration Level, lb salt/cu ft	Softening Capacity*, kilograin ($CaCO_3$)/cu ft	Salt Regeneration Efficiency, lb NaCl/kilogram
5	15.4	0.32
10	24.0	0.41
15	29.4	0.51
20	32.3	0.62
25	34.2	0.73
30	35.4	0.85

* Capacity to a 5 ppm hardness leakage.

Solution:

From the data in Table A.1, the water to be softened has a total hardness (Ca + Mg) of 200 parts per million (200 ppm) or $\frac{200}{17.1}$ = 11.7 grains per gallon [17.1 ppm = 1 grain ($CaCO_3$) per gallon]. Since 20,000 gallons of water are to be treated per day, 20,000 × 11.7 = 234,000 grains or 234 kilograins of hardness (as $CaCO_3$) must be removed daily (1000 grains = 1 kilogram). From the data of Table A.2, it can be seen that at a regeneration level of 5 lb of salt per cubic foot of resin, a capacity of 15.4 kilogram cu ft can be realized at high salt efficiency. Therefore, $\frac{234}{15.4}$ = 15.2 cu ft of resin will be required. The data in Table A.2 indicate that less resin is required if more regenerant is used. For example, at approximately half the salt efficiency, 20 lb of salt will yield a capacity of 32.3 kilogram and $\frac{234}{32.3}$ = 7.2 cu ft of resin are required. It is therefore quite apparent that in any design considerations there is a balance between regeneration cost and equipment and resin costs. By increasing the regeneration level, one can decrease the capital investment.

In formulating the design of large installations, there are other factors to be considered. For example, if treated water storage facilities are not available for needs during the regeneration period, a stand-by ion exchange unit will be required. In addition, provisions must be made for the capacity deterioration of certain resins, particularly anion exchange resins.

Since there exists a pressure drop across a bed of an ion exchanger, consideration must be given to the ratio of the diameter to the height of the bed of exchanger. Since all resin manufacturers publish hydraulic data for their standard exchangers, one can readily calculate the pressure drop across an ion exchange bed of any dimensions and under any flow rate conditions.

Table A.3 illustrates typical pressure drop data for a standard high capacity sulfonic acid cation exchange resin. The following problem illustrates the calculation necessary to calculate the headloss or pressure drop across a bed of resin for a given condition.

TABLE A.3. PRESSURE DROP CHARACTERISTICS OF A TYPICAL
HIGH CAPACITY SULFONIC ACID CATION EXCHANGE RESIN

Flow Rate in gal/sq ft (bed diameter)/min.	Pressure Drop, psi/ft of bed depth		
	35°F	50°F	75°F
2	0.36	0.28	0.20
4	0.72	0.56	0.40
6	1.08	0.84	0.60
8	1.44	1.12	0.80
10	1.80	1.40	1.00

Problem:

What is the pressure drop across a bed of a resin 5 ft in depth at 50°F at a flow rate of 6 gal/sq ft/min.?

Solution:

According to the data in Table A.3, the pressure drop (ΔP) will be 0.84 psi/ft. The pressure drop across the entire bed will be

$$\Delta P = 0.84 \times 5 = 4.20 \text{ psi.}$$

It is important to note that the pressure drop will decrease with an increase in temperature.

Since the design of an ion-exchange unit must allow sufficient room for the expansion of the exchange bed during the backwashing portion of the cycle, it is essential to know the hydraulic expansion characteristics of each exchanger bed. Again, the resin manufacturer supplies the necessary hydraulic expansion data for their standard products. The data in Table A.4 are typical. The problem described below is indicative of a typical design calculation involving a back-wash operation.

TABLE A.4. HYDRAULIC EXPANSION DATA FOR A TYPICAL
HIGH CAPACITY SULFONIC ACID CATION EXCHANGE RESIN

Flow Rate in gal./sq ft/min.	% Expansion of Resin Bed (72°F)		
	50°F	72°F	90°F
2	20	12	8
4	50	33	25
6	75	54	45
8	> 100	75	66
10	> 100	95	87

Problem:

Approximately what flow rates are required, according to the data in Table A.4, to achieve 75 per cent backwash expansion at temperatures of 50°F and 72°F, respectively?

Solution:

According to the data of Table A.4, at a temperature of 50°F, 75 per cent bed expansion is achieved at a flow rate of 6 gal./sq ft/min. At a temperature of 72°F, a flow rate of 8 gal./sq ft/min. is required for the same expansion. The sensitivity of expansion with change in temperature is most important in the design of ion exchange units that will operate satisfactorily over the entire range in temperature that will be experienced all year round.

Problem:

What is the minimum regeneration level required to maintain a softened water effluent of approximately 20 ppm (as $CaCo_3$) if the influent hardness level is 400 ppm (as $CaCO_3$)?

Solution:

Using the data in Figure 6.3, it is apparent that at a level of 1 lb of salt per cubic foot, the hardness leakage is approximately 25 ppm and at 2 lb of salt, the leakage is well below 10 ppm. One can therefore employ a regenerant level that is approximately 1¼ lb in order to achieve the desired effluent quality.

In the case of deionization, one is faced with the use of two resins, an anion and a cation exchange resin. The following problem and solution is a typical example.

Problem:

If one is to deionize a water containing 500 ppm of NaCl (as $CaCO_3$) to the extent that the effluent contains less than 50 ppm NaCl (as $CaCO_3$), what are the minimum regenerant levels required for both resins and what capacities will be realized by each resin?

Solution:

By referring to the information in Chapter 6, it is evident that for the partial removal of such constituents as sodium chloride one needs but use a two-bed system involving a strong acid cation exchanger and a weak base anion exchanger. The maximum leakage required is 50 ppm and therefore $\frac{50}{500} \times 100 = 10\%$ maximum leakage. By referring to Figure 6.4, it is evident that a minimum of 17 lb of 66° Bé sulfuric acid are required and that a capacity of 34 kg per cu ft will be realized. For the weak base anion exchanger, it is evident from Figure 6.5 that approximately 3 to 4 lb of caustic per cubic foot are required and that the capacity will be 29 kilograin/cu ft. Since the 500 ppm water contains $\frac{500}{17.1} = 29$

grains per gallon, a cubic foot of the cation exchanger will treat $\frac{34 \times 1000}{29} = 1,200$ gal. and the anion exchanger will treat $\frac{29}{29} \times 1000 = 1,000$ gal. To maintain a balanced system, one will have to employ $\frac{1,200}{1,000} = 1.2$ cu ft of anion exchanger per cu ft of cation exchanger used.

HELPFUL OPERATIONAL HINTS

The operation of most ion exchange installations that are properly designed and engineered is normally uneventful and trouble-free. However, full utilization of an ion-exchange unit demands a proper understanding of the properties of the exchanger and the necessary experience to handle certain unforeseen happenings.

Exchanger Stability

Although most ion-exchange materials are considered as capital equipment in many installations, all ion exchange materials suffer both physical and chemical degradation and their useful life is usually less than the life of the equipment. The anion-exchange resins are normally the least stable of all ion-exchange materials and their useful life varies from 500,000 to 2,000,000 gallons treated per cubic foot of exchanger. Under normal conditions, the degradation experienced with anion exchangers is chemical in nature (oxidation) and a gradual loss in exchange capacity is experienced during the useful life of the resin. Any design considerations must take this factor into consideration.

In the case of cation exchange resins, particularly, the high capacity sulfonic acid materials, very little capacity loss is experienced during the life of the exchanger which usually varies between 2,000,000 and 10,000,000 gallons treated per cubic foot of resin. The nature of the degradation is either one of physical breakdown due to attrition or decross-linking due to oxidative attack. The resin is usually replaced when it has either become too fine in particle size because of attrition or after it has become jelly-like in character due to decross-linking.

The life of the ion-exchange resins can be prolonged if oxidative conditions can be minimized or eliminated. Employment of lower temperatures and elimination of oxygen, chlorine and oxidative catalysts such as trace quantities of copper and iron are recommended whenever possible. The life of siliceous cation exchangers can be kept at reasonable levels only when their use is limited to neutral (neither alkaline nor acidic) waters containing a few parts per million of silica.

Exchanger Fouling

Ion-exchange materials, at times, lose their effectiveness due to the accumulation of materials on their surfaces and in their pores. This accumulation of material, or fouling, is a result of an adsorption of colloids and high molecular weight ionic species which is not completely removed during the normal backwash and regeneration steps of the cycle. The substances that frequently foul ion exchangers are the traces of iron, clay, humic acids, tannins, and silica that are present in untreated surface water supplies. As they accumulate on and in the exchangers, they clog the pores and impair the effectiveness by reducing the rates of exchange. The fouling of exchangers can be minimized by proper water pretreatment practices which include coagulation, filtration, chlorination, etc. The accumulation of colloids on the surfaces of exchangers can be minimized by good backwash techniques. Controlled and proper backwash procedures are an essential part of the ion-exchange operation and their importance cannot be overemphasized.

The accumulation of iron on the surface of cation exchangers used in water softening operations can be minimized by the addition of a small quantity of a reducing agent such as sodium hydrosulfite to the brine regenerant. Ion exchange resins that have been neglected and have accumulated large quantities of colloidal iron can only be restored by acid treatment. Anion exchange resins fouled with large amounts of aged, colloidal silica can be rejuvenated by treatment with warm caustic solutions. Quaternary ammonium (strong base) anion exchange resins which are fouled with organic matter such as humic and tannic acids can be restored by warm brine treatments or by an occasional sodium hypochlorite wash. To date, experience has shown that fouling problems are best handled by good preventative measures, i.e., water pretreatment, proper backwashing, and early rejuvenation procedures.

Trouble-Shooting

On occasion, one finds that an ion exchange installation is not performing as it should be and that no simple explanation can be found. In such instances, the difficulty can only be ascertained by means of a thorough "check-out." The source of difficulty can only be due to one of three possibilities; i.e., (1) change in nature of the solution being fed to the ion exchange unit, (2) a failure or defect in the equipment, and (3) a change in the operating characteristics of the exchanger. All three possibilities must be considered separately.

In checking for changes in the nature of the influent, analyses must be made in order to ascertain if new troublesome ionic species or colloids have entered the influent.

It is also possible that the concentration of the ions being removed have increased in concentration. For example, it is important to realize that, in the treatment of water supplies, the composition of the raw water, particularly surface waters, varies considerably between summer and winter and before and after heavy rainfalls. These changes can alter the operating characteristics of the ion exchange units. Periodic checks on the nature of the influent to an ion exchange unit should be made in order that these difficulties can be anticipated.

Minor failures or defects in the ion exchange equipment are at times quite troublesome and a source of considerable difficulty. It is for this reason that periodic checks on the equipment are most important. Large units usually contain sample points in order that the trouble spot can be readily isolated and the difficulty repaired. The three most trouble-producing spots in the equipment are (1) the multiport valve where improper seating can result in a bleeding of influent or regenerant into the effluent, (2) distributors (upper and lower) where clogging results in by-passing or channeling, and (3) the underdrain where clogging also results in poor liquid distribution, channeling, and poor backwashing.

Should the check-out indicate that the exchanger is at fault, the unit must be opened and samples must be removed for inspection and analysis according to the procedures outlined in Chapter 4. The sample must be taken so that a representative sampling is assured.

In large installations where shut-downs can be very serious, periodic check-outs as described above are an insurance against trouble.

APPENDIX 2

TERMINOLOGY

The following are the definition of some symbols and terms frequently employed in ion exchange:

Anion Exchange Capacity (A.E.C.): The ultimate exchange capacity of an anion exchange material, usually expressed as milliequivalents per gram or milliliter of exchanger.

Cation Exchange Capacity (C.E.C.): The ultimate exchange capacity of a cation exchange material, usually expressed as milliequivalents per gram or milliliter of exchanger.

Breakthrough Capacity: Capacity of an ion exchange column at any fixed arbitrary endpoint and at a fixed regeneration level, usually expressed as kilograins per cubic foot of exchanger.

Saturation Column Capacity: Capacity of an ion exchange column when fully saturated, usually expressed as kilograins per cubic foot.

C: Concentration of effluent.

Co: Concentration of influent.

Influent: Liquid entering ion exchange column.

Effluent: Liquid leaving ion exchange column.

Regeneration: Restoring resin to state employed for adsorption.

Regeneration Level: Quantity of regenerant employed.

Regeneration Efficiency: Regeneration level ÷ breakthrough capacity.

Leakage: $C/C_0 \times 100$.

Loading Curve: A plot of breakthrough capacity as a function of regeneration level.

Elution: Process of removing ions adsorbed on exchanger column.

Eluant: Solution employed for elution.

Eluate: Effluent during elution.

TYPICAL COMMERCIAL ION EXCHANGE RESINS

Trade Name	Type	Manufacturer	Approximate Capacity	
			meq/g	meq/ml
Cation Exchangers				
"Amberlite" IR-120	Sulfonic	Rohm & Haas Co.	4.5	2.0
"Dowex 50"	"	Dow Chemical Co.		
"Duolite" C-20	"	Chemical Process Co.		
"Permutit" Q	"	Pfaudler-Permutit Co.		
"Amberlite" IRC-50	Carboxylic	Rohm & Haas Co.	10	4.0
Anion Exchangers				
"Amberlite" IRA-400	Quaternary	Rohm & Haas Co.	3.5	1.3
"Dowex" 1	"	Dow Chemical Co.		
"Amberlite" IR-45	Polyamine	Rohm & Haas Co.	5.0	2.0
"Dowex" 3	"	Dow Chemical Co.		

ION EXCHANGE CALCULATION AND CONVERSION FACTORS

1 grain per U.S. gallon = 17.1 parts per million (ppm)
1 kilograin = 1000 grains
1 cubic foot = 28.3 liters
1 gallon (U.S.) = 3.785 liters
1 gal./cu ft/min. = 0.134 cc/cc/min.
1 lb/cu ft = 0.016 gram/cc

Screen Sizes

Screen No.	U.S. Standard		Sieve Openings	Tyler	
	in.	mm		mm	in.
12	0.0661	1.68		1.397	0.055
16	0.0469	1.19		0.991	0.039
20	0.0331	0.84		0.833	0.0328
30	0.0232	0.59	(24 mesh)	0.589	0.0232
40	0.0165	0.42	(42 mesh)	0.351	0.0138
50	0.0117	0.297	(48 mesh)	0.295	0.0116
70	0.0083	0.210		—	—
100	0.0059	0.149		0.147	0.0058

Table of Chemical Elements

Element	Symbol	Atomic No.	Atomic Wt.	Element	Symbol	Atomic No.	Atomic Wt.
Actinium	Ac	89	227.	Gadolinium	Gd	64	157.26
Aluminum	Al	13	26.98	Gallium	Ga	31	69.72
Americium	Am	95	243.	Germanium	Ge	32	72.60
Antimony	Sb	51	121.76	Gold	Au	79	197.0
Argon	Ar	18	39.94	Hafnium	Hf	72	178.50
Arsenic	As	33	74.92	Helium	He	2	4.00
Astatine	At	85	210.	Holmium	Ho	67	164.94
Barium	Ba	56	137.36	Hydrogen	H	1	1.01
Berkelium	Bk	97	249.	Indium	In	49	114.82
Beryllium	Be	4	9.01	Iodine	I	53	126.91
Bismuth	Bi	83	208.99	Iridium	Ir	77	192.2
Boron	B	5	10.82	Iron	Fe	26	55.85
Bromine	Br	35	79.92	Krypton	Kr	36	83.80
Cadmium	Cd	48	112.41	Lanthanum	La	57	138.92
Calcium	Ca	20	40.08	Lead	Pb	82	207.21
Californium	Cf	98	251.	Lithium	Li	3	6.94
Carbon	C	6	12.01	Lutetium	Lu	71	174.99
Cerium	Ce	58	140.13	Magnesium	Mg	12	24.32
Cesium	Cs	55	132.91	Manganese	Mn	25	54.94
Chlorine	Cl	17	35.46	Mendelevium	Md	101	256.
Chromium	Cr	24	52.01	Mercury	Hg	80	200.61
Cobalt	Co	27	58.94	Molybdenum	Mo	42	95.95
Copper	Cu	29	63.54	Neodymium	Nd	60	144.27
Curium	Cm	96	247.	Neon	Ne	10	20.18
Dysprosium	Dy	66	162.51	Neptunium	Np	93	237.
Einsteinium	Es	99	254.	Nickel	Ni	28	58.71
Erbium	Er	68	167.27	Niobium	Nb	41	92.91
Europium	Eu	63	152.0	Nitrogen	N	7	14.01
Fermium	Fm	100	253.0	Nobelium	No	102	254.
Fluorine	F	9	19.00	Osmium	Os	76	190.2
Francium	Fr	87	223.	Oxygen	O	8	16.00

TABLE OF CHEMICAL ELEMENTS—*Continued*

Element	Symbol	Atomic No.	Atomic Wt.	Element	Symbol	Atomic No.	Atomic Wt.
Palladium	Pd	46	106.4	Sodium	Na	11	22.99
Phosphorus	P	15	30.96	Strontium	Sr	38	87.63
Platinum	Pt	78	195.09	Sulfur	S	16	32.07
Plutonium	Pu	94	242.	Tantalum	Ta	73	180.95
Polonium	Po	84	210.	Technetium	Tc	43	99.
Potassium	K	19	39.10	Tellurium	Te	52	127.61
Praseodymium	Pr	59	140.91	Terbium	Tb	65	158.93
Promethium	Pm	61	147.	Thallium	Tl	81	204.39
Protactinium	Pa	91	231.	Thorium	Th	90	232.
Radium	Ra	88	226.	Thulium	Tm	69	168.94
Radon	Rn	86	222.	Tin	Sn	50	118.70
Rhenium	Re	75	186.22	Titanium	Ti	22	47.90
Rhodium	Rh	45	102.91	Tungsten	W	74	183.86
Rubidium	Rb	37	85.48	Uranium	U	92	238.
Ruthenium	Ru	44	101.1	Vanadium	V	23	50.95
Samarium	Sm	62	150.35	Xenon	Xe	54	131.30
Scandium	Sc	21	44.96	Ytterbium	Yb	70	173.04
Selenium	Se	34	78.96	Yttrium	Y	39	88.91
Silicon	Si	14	28.09	Zinc	Zn	30	65.38
Silver	Ag	47	107.88	Zirconium	Zr	40	91.22

APPENDIX 3

SELECTED READING

I. *History of Ion Exchange*

1. Kelley, W. F., "Cation Exchange in Soils," Reinhold Publishing Corp., New York, 1948.
2. Thompson, H. S., *J. Roy. Agr. Soc. England,* 11, 68 (1850).
3. Way, J. T., *J. Roy. Agr. Soc. England,* 11, 313 (1850).

II. *Nature of Ion Exchange*

1. Glueckauf, E., *Endeavor,* 14, 54 (1955).
2. "Ion Exchange and Its Applications," *Soc. Chem. Ind.,* London (1955).
3. Kunin, R., "Ion Exchange Resins," 2nd Ed., J. Wiley & Sons, Inc., New York, 1958.
4. Reichenberg, D. and McCauley, D., *J. Chem. Soc.,* 2741 (1955).

III. *Synthesis of Ion Exchange Materials*

1. Adams, B. A. and Holmes, E. L., *J. Soc. Chem. Ind.,* 54, 1-6T (1935).
2. Billmeyer, F. W., Jr., "Textbook of Polymer Chemistry," Interscience Publishers, Inc., New York, 1957.

3. Bodamer, G., U. S. Patents 2,681,319 and 2,681,320 (6-15-54).

4. D'Alelio, G. F., U. S. Patents 2,366,007 (12-26-44) and 2,340,110 (1-25-44).

5. McBurney, C. H., U. S. Patents 2,591,573 (4-1-52) and 2,291,574 (4-1-52).

IV. *General Books on Ion Exchange*

1. Kitchener, J. A., "Ion Exchange Resins," Methuen & Company, London, 1957.

2. Kunin, R., "Ion Exchange Resins," J. Wiley & Sons, Inc., New York, 1958.

3. Nachod, F., "Ion Exchange," Academic Press, Inc., New York, 1949.

4. Nachod, F. and Schubert, J., "Ion Exchange Technology," Academic Press, Inc., New York, 1957.

5. Osborn, G., "Synthetic Ion Exchangers," Chapman & Hall, London, 1955.

V. *Books on Ion Exchange in Medicine, Organic Chemistry and Biochemistry*

1. Calmon, C. and Kressman, T. R. E., "Ion Exchangers in Organic and Biochemistry," Interscience Publishers, Inc., New York, 1957.

2. Martin, G. J., "Ion Exchange and Adsorptive Agents in Medicine," Little, Brown & Company, Boston, 1954.

VI. *Ion Exchange in Atomic Energy*

1. Clegg, J. W. and Foley, D. D., "Uranium Ore Processing," Addison-Wesley, Reading, Mass. (1958).

2. Kunin, R. and Preuss, A., *Ind. Eng. Chem.,* **48,** 30A (1956).

3. "Uranium in South Africa, 1946-56," Vol. 1 and 2—The Assoc. Sci. and Tech. Soc. of South Africa, Johannesburg, South Africa, 1957.

VII. *Ion Exchange in Analytical Chemistry*

1. Samuelson, O., "Ion Exchangers in Analytical Chemistry," J. Wiley & Sons, Inc., New York, 1953.

INDEX